C000193136

EASIEST
KEYBOARD
COLLECTION

Big Chart Hits

WISE PUBLICATIONS
London/New York/Paris/Sydney/Copenhagen/Berlin/Madrid/Tokyo

Exclusive Distributors:

Music Sales Limited
8/9 Frith Street,
London W1D 3JB, England.

Music Sales Pty Limited
120 Rothschild Avenue,
Rosebery, NSW 2018,
Australia.

Order No. AM972070
ISBN 0-7119-9086-7
This book © Copyright 2002 by Wise Publications

Compiled by Nick Crispin
Music arranged by Roger Day & Derek Jones
Music processed by Paul Ewers Music Design
Cover design by Chloë Alexander
Printed and bound in Malta.

Your Guarantee of Quality
As publishers, we strive to produce every book to the highest
commercial standards.
This book has been carefully designed to minimise awkward page
turns and to make playing from it a real pleasure.
Particular care has been given to specifying acid-free, neutral-sized
paper made from pulps which have not been elemental chlorine
bleached. This pulp is from farmed sustainable forests and was
produced with special regard for the environment.
Throughout, the printing and binding have been planned to ensure
a sturdy, attractive publication which should give years
of enjoyment.
If your copy fails to meet our high standards, please inform us
and we will gladly replace it.

www.musicsales.com

Contents

AGAINST ALL ODDS
(TAKE A LOOK AT ME NOW)

Words & Music by Phil Collins

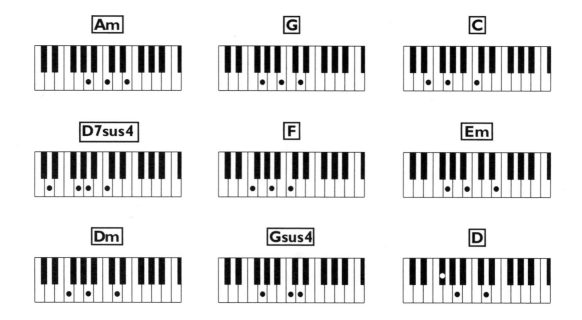

Voice: **Synth Lead 2**

Rhythm: **Epic Ballad**

Tempo: ♩ = **66**

How can I just let you walk a-way, just let you leave with-out a trace? When I stand here tak-in' ev'-ry breath, with

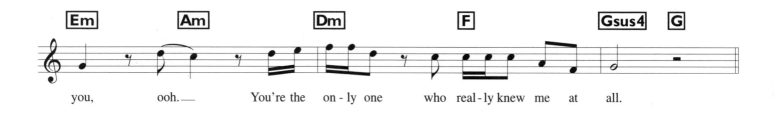

you,   ooh.___   You're the on-ly one   who real-ly knew me at all.

How can you just walk a-way from me, when all I can do is watch you leave? Cos we've shared the laugh-ter and the pain   and

4

BLACK COFFEE

Words & Music by Tom Nichols, Alexander Soos & Kirsty Elizabeth

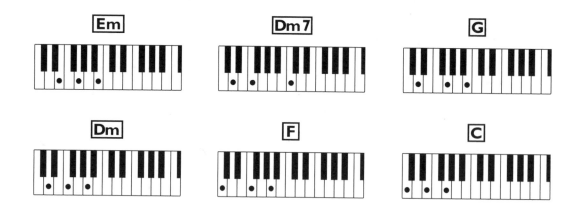

Voice: **Harp**

Rhythm: **8 Beat Pop**

Tempo: ♩ = 120

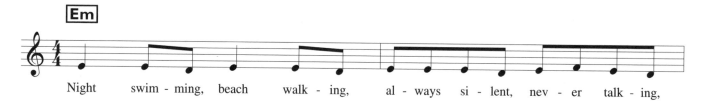

Night swim-ming, beach walk-ing, al-ways si-lent, nev-er talk-ing,

then you call my name and I know in-side I love you. Sail a-way, I miss you more un-

-til you see the shore. There I will be wait-ing, an-ti-ci-pat-ing.

Each mo-ment is new, freeze the mo-ment.

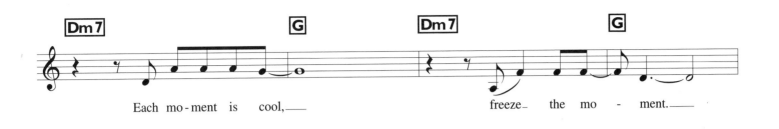

Each mo-ment is cool,___ freeze_ the mo - ment.___

I would-n't wan-na be a - ny - where_ else_ but here.___

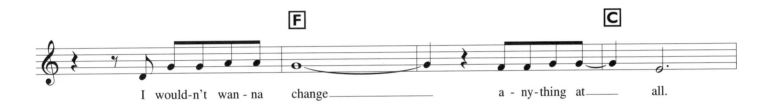

I would-n't wan - na change_____ a - ny-thing at___ all.

(A - ny - thing_ ah.) I would-n't wan - na take ev - 'ry - thing_ out_ on

you,_____ though I know I do,_____ (al - though I

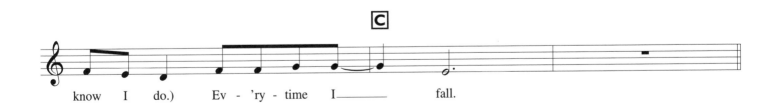

know I do.) Ev - 'ry - time I_____ fall.

Repeat to fade

CAN YOU FEEL THE LOVE TONIGHT
(FROM WALT DISNEY PICTURES' "THE LION KING")

Music by Elton John
Words by Tim Rice

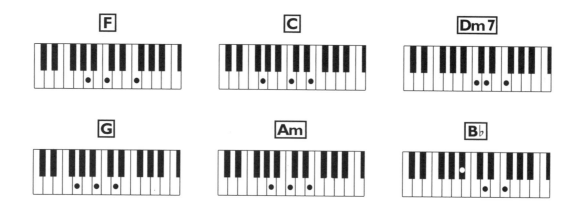

Voice: **Electric Piano 2**

Rhythm: **Pop Ballad**

Tempo: ♩ = 104

There's a calm sur - ren - der to the rush of day,

when the heat of the roll - ing world can be turned a - way.

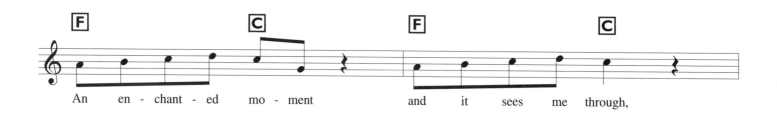

An en - chant - ed mo - ment and it sees me through,

it's e - nough for this rest - less war - rior, just to be with you. And

DANCING IN THE MOONLIGHT

Words & Music by Sherman Kelly
© Copyright 1970 EMI Catalogue Partnership Limited/EMI U Catalog Incorporated/Saint Nathanson Music Limited.
Worldwide print rights controlled by Warner Bros. Publications Incorporated/IMP Limited. Used with permission.
All Rights Reserved. International Copyright Secured.

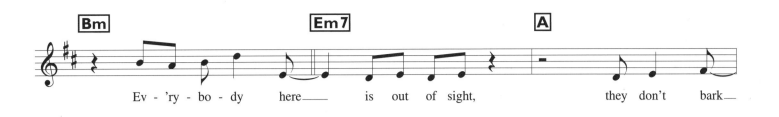

Ev - 'ry - bo - dy here___ is out of sight, they don't bark___

___ and they___ don't bite,___ they keep___ things loose,___

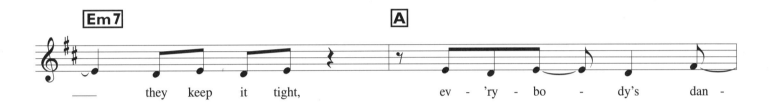

___ they keep it tight, ev - 'ry - bo - dy's dan -

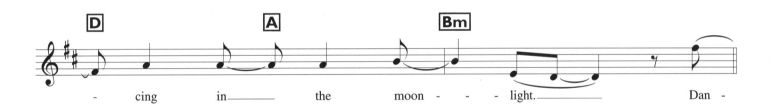

- cing in___ the moon - - light.___ Dan -

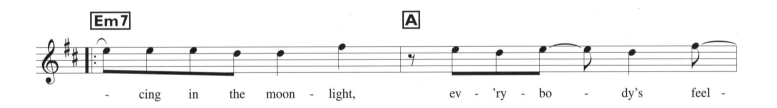

- cing in the moon - light, ev - 'ry - bo - dy's feel -

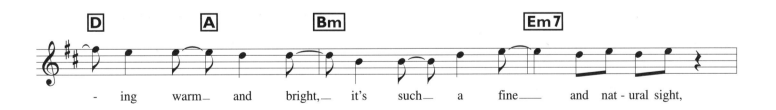

- ing warm___ and bright,___ it's such___ a fine___ and nat - ural sight,

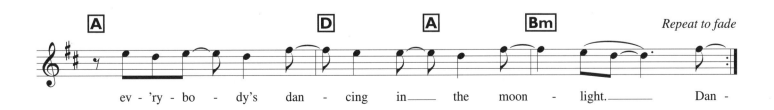

Repeat to fade

ev - 'ry - bo - dy's dan - cing in___ the moon - light. Dan -

DEEPER SHADE OF BLUE

Words & Music by Mark Topham & Karl Twigg

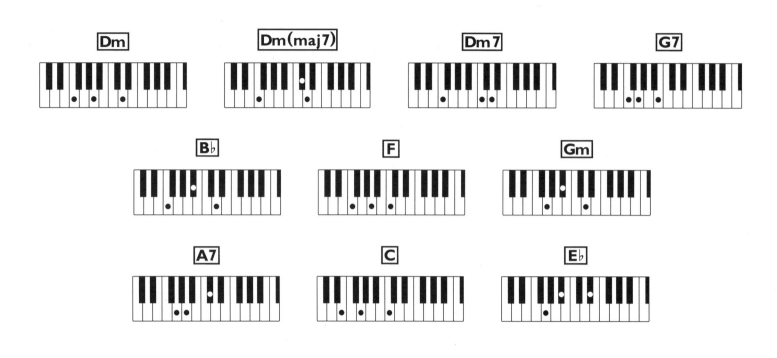

Voice: **Electric Guitar**

Rhythm: **Pop Ballad**

Tempo: ♩ = 126

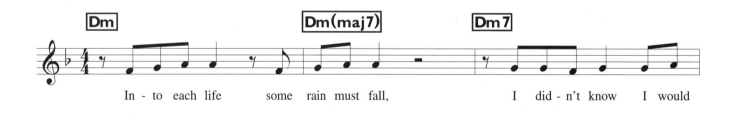

In - to each life some rain must fall, I did - n't know I would

catch it all. The clear skies have gone and you with them too,

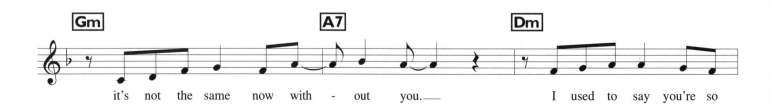

it's not the same now with - out you. I used to say you're so

beau - ti - ful,   but it did - n't change a   thing at all.   There's no -

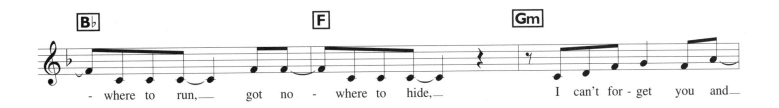

- where to run,___ got no - where to hide,___   I can't for - get you and___

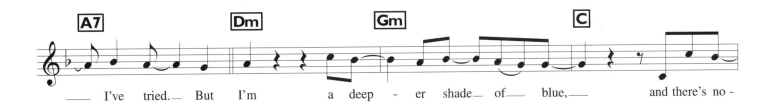

___ I've tried. But I'm   a deep - er shade__ of__ blue,___   and there's no -

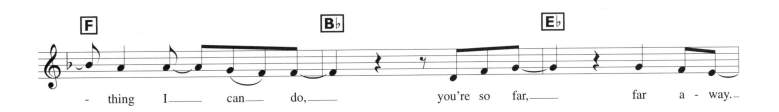

- thing I___ can do,___   you're so far,___   far a - way.___

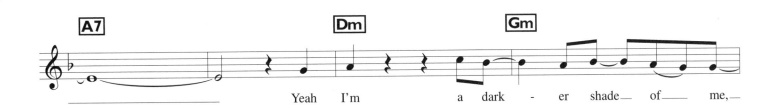

___   Yeah I'm   a dark - er shade__ of___ me,___

___ and I___ just can't__ be free,___   you're so far,___

___ far a - way,_____ you're so far a - way.___

A DESIGN FOR LIFE

Words & Music by Nicky Wire, James Dean Bradfield & Sean Moore

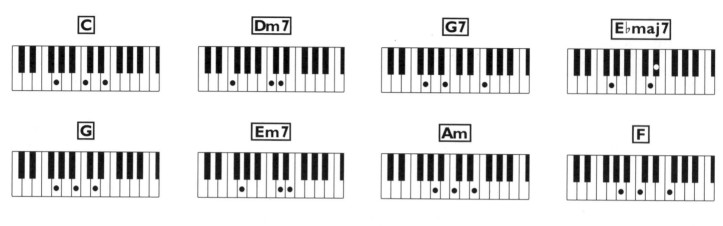

Voice: **Electric Piano 2**

Rhythm: **Funky Pop I**

Tempo: ♩ = 92

Libraries gave us pow - er,   then work came and made us

free.   What price___ now.   for___ a shal - low

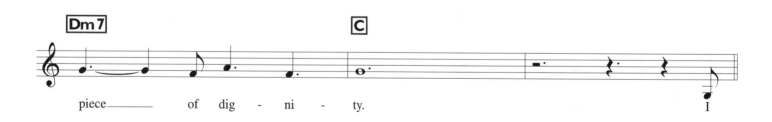

piece___ of dig - ni - ty.   I

wish I had a bot - tle___   right here in my dir - ty

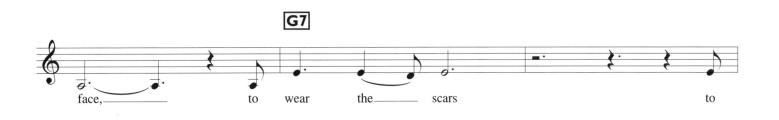

face,_____ to wear the_____ scars to

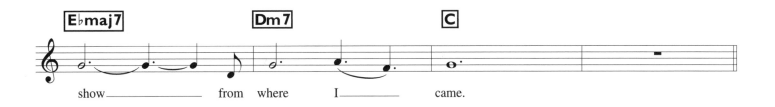

show_____ from where I_____ came.

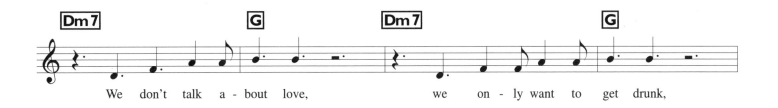

We don't talk a - bout love, we on - ly want to get drunk,

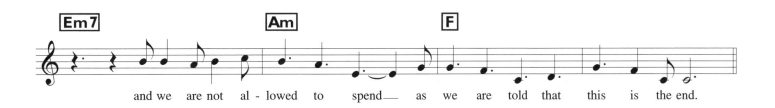

and we are not al - lowed to spend___ as we are told that this is the end.

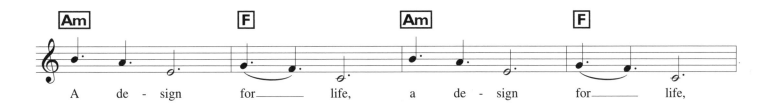

A de - sign for_____ life, a de - sign for_____ life,

a de - sign for_____ life, a de - sign for life.

DON'T STOP MOVIN'

Words & Music by Simon Ellis, Sheppard Solomon & S Club 7

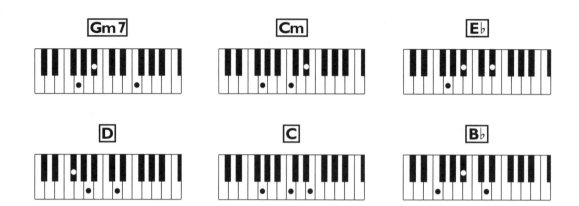

Voice: **Brass Ensemble**

Rhythm: **Funky Pop 2**

Tempo: ♩ = 120

Don't stop mov-in' to the fun-ky, fun-ky beat. Don't stop mov-in' to the fun-ky, fun-ky beat.

D. J. got the par-ty start-ed, there's no end in sight, ev - 'ry-bo-dy's mov-in' to the rhy-thm that's in-side, it's a cra-

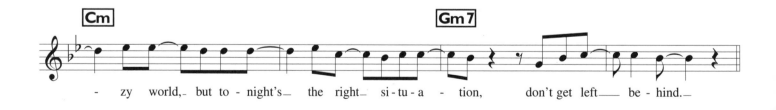

- zy world,_ but to - night's_ the right_ si - tu - a - tion, don't get left_ be - hind._

I can feel the mu - sic mov-in' through me ev - 'ry-where, ain't_ no des - ti - na-tion, ba - by,

we don't ev - en care. There's a place___ to be___ if you need___ the right___ ed - u - ca -

- tion, let me take___ you there.___ And just go___ with the ma - gic, ba - by,

I can see it there in your eyes, ___ let it flow,___ stop___ the wait - ing

right here on the dance floor is where you got-ta let it go. Don't___ stop mov-in', can___ you feel the mu-sic? D.___

___ J. got us go-in' a - round,___ round.___ Don't___ stop mov- in', find___ your own way to it, list -

- en to the mu - sic, tak - ing you to pla - ces that you've nev - er been be - fore, ba - by now.___

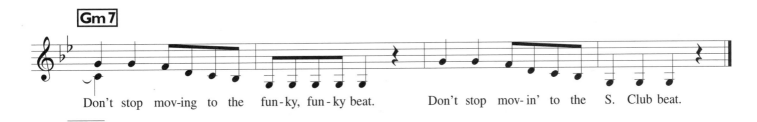

Don't stop mov-ing to the fun-ky, fun-ky beat. Don't stop mov-in' to the S. Club beat.

ETERNITY

Words & Music by Robbie Williams & Guy Chambers
© Copyright 2001 BMG Music Publishing Limited /
EMI Music Publishing Limited.

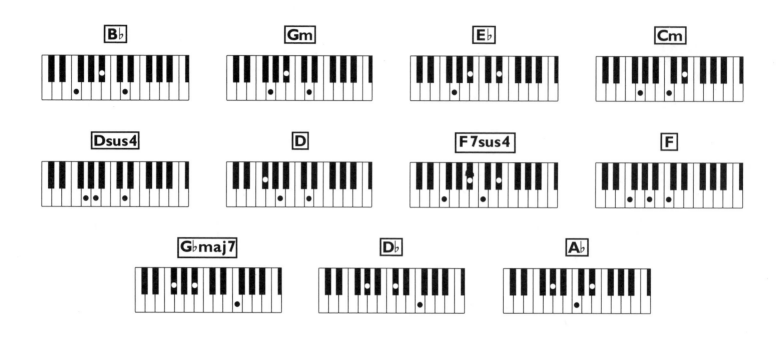

Voice: **Piano 1**

Rhythm: **Soft Rock 2**

Tempo: ♩ = **76**

Close your eyes— so you don't feel them, they don't need to see— you

cry.   I can't pro - mise   I will heal you,

but if you want— to I will   try.   I sing this sum - mer se - ren - ade,— the

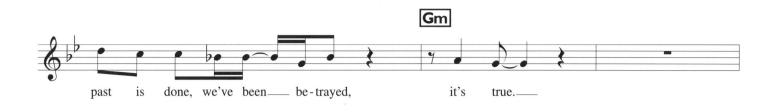
past is done, we've been be-trayed, it's true.

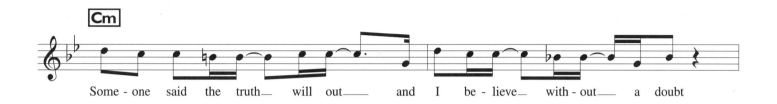
Some-one said the truth will out and I be-lieve with-out a doubt

in you. You were there for sum-mer dream - ing and you

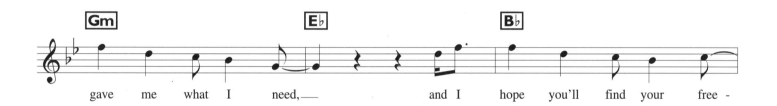
gave me what I need, and I hope you'll find your free -

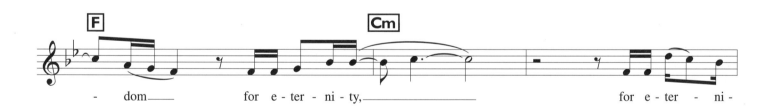
- dom for e-ter-ni-ty, for e-ter-ni-

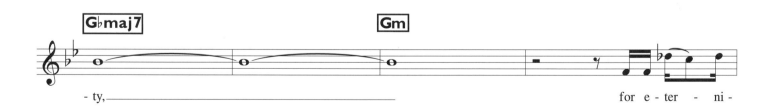
- ty, for e-ter-ni-

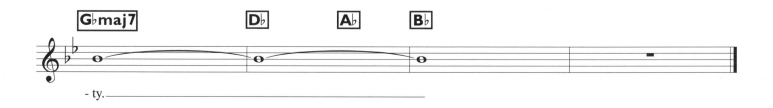
- ty.

GIVE ME A REASON

Words & Music by Andrea Corr, Caroline Corr, Sharon Corr & Jim Corr

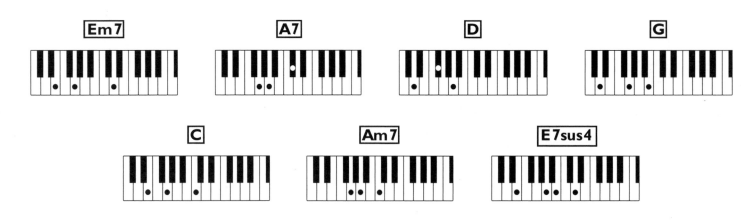

Voice: **Electric Guitar**

Rhythm: **Pop Rock 1**

Tempo: ♩ = 116

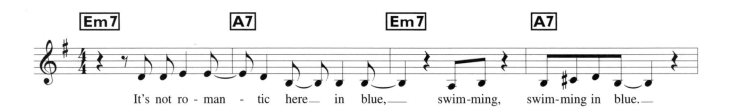

It's not ro-man-tic here— in blue,— swim-ming, swim-ming in blue.—

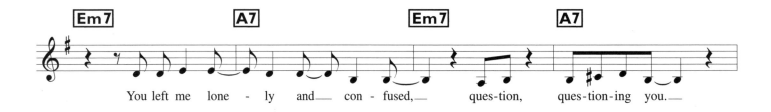

You left me lone-ly and— con-fused,— ques-tion, ques-tion-ing you.—

So soon good-bye,— you stole— my heart,— I'm be-lieve, I'm be-liev-ing you.—

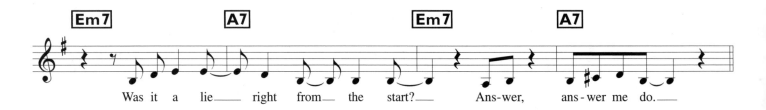

Was it a lie— right from— the start?— Ans-wer, ans-wer me do.—

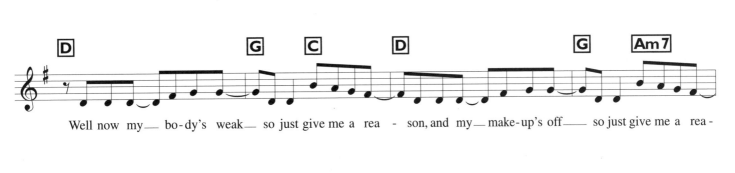

Well now my — bo-dy's weak — so just give me a rea - son, and my — make-up's off — so just give me a rea-

- son, my de - fence is down — so just give me a rea - son, I am — strong e - nough

—— so give me a rea - son, my bo-dy is weak — so just give me a rea-

- son, and my — make-up's off — so just give me a rea - son, my de - fence is down

—— so just give me a rea - son, give me a rea - son, give me a rea - son, ——

give me a rea - son, —— give me a rea - son, ——

give me a rea - son. —— What did I do — wrong? ——

GO LET IT OUT

Words & Music by Noel Gallagher

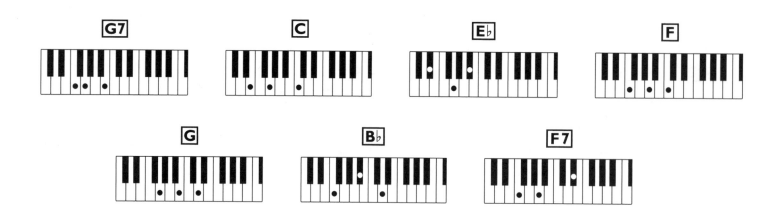

Voice: **Tenor Saxophone**

Rhythm: **Pop Rock 1**

Tempo: ♩ = 84

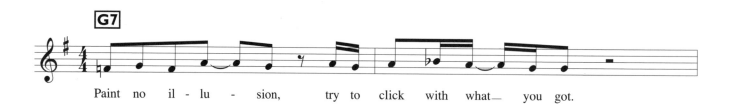

Paint no il-lu-sion, try to click with what— you got.

Taste ev-ery po-tion, 'cause if you like your-self— a-lot. Go let it

out, go let it in, and go let it out.

Life is pre-co-cious in the most pe-cu-liar way, sis-ter psy-cho-sis, don't

I WANT IT THAT WAY

Words & Music by Max Martin & Andreas Carlsson
© Copyright 1999 Zomba Music Publishers Limited.
All Rights Reserved. International Copyright Secured.

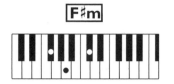
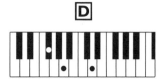
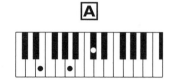
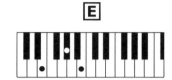

Voice: **Acoustic Guitar**

Rhythm: **Lite Pop**

Tempo: ♩ = 104

You are ———— my fi - re, —— the one ——

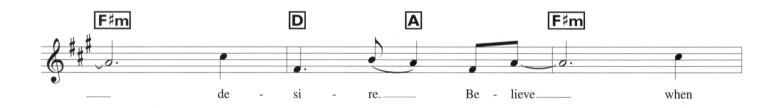

—— de - si - re. —— Be - lieve —— when

I say, —— I want —— it that - a way. —— But we

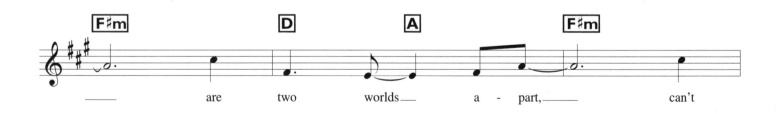

—— are two worlds —— a - part, —— can't

reach to —— your heart, —— when you say —— that

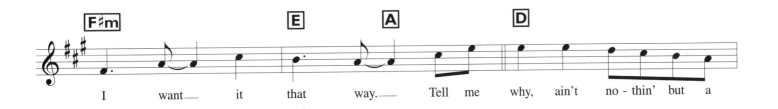

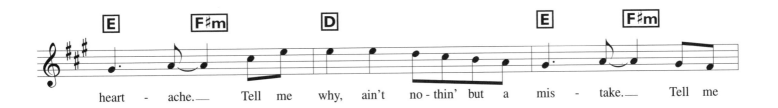

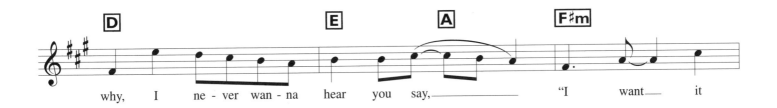

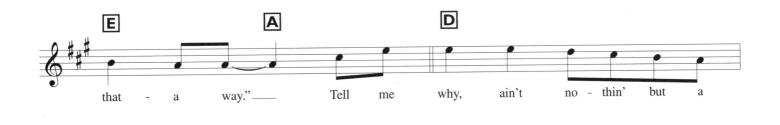

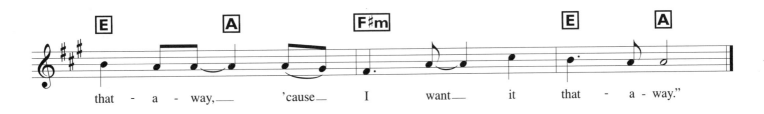

I'M OUTTA LOVE

Words & Music by Anastacia, Sam Watters & Louis Biancaniello

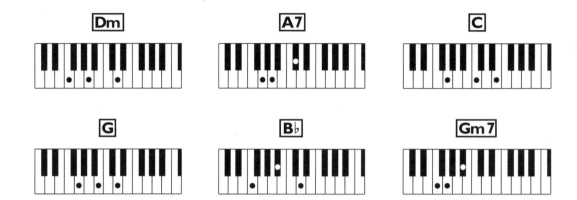

Voice:	**Brass/String Layer**
Rhythm:	**16 Beat Funk**
Tempo:	♩ = 98

Now ba - by come on, ___ don't claim ___

___ that love_ you nev - er let_ me feel. ___ I should have known

___ 'cause you've_ brought no - thing_ real. ___ Come on, be a man

___ a - bout_ it. You_ won't_ die. ___ I ___ ain't got no more tears ___

KEEP ON MOVIN'

Words & Music by Richard Stannard, Julian Gallagher,
Richard Breen, Sean Conlon & Jason Brown

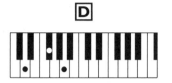 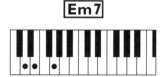  

Voice: **Strings/Guitar Layer**

Rhythm: **Pop Rock 2**

Tempo: ♩ = 124

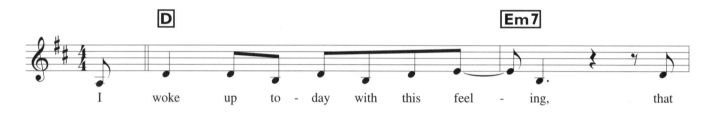

I woke up to - day with this feel - ing, that

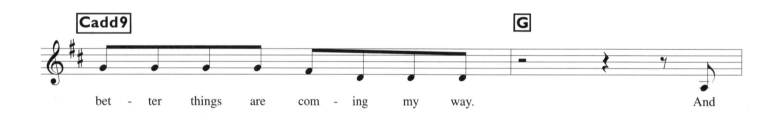

bet - ter things are com - ing my way. And

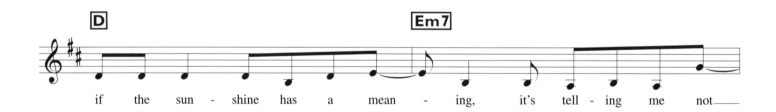

if the sun - shine has a mean - ing, it's tell - ing me not

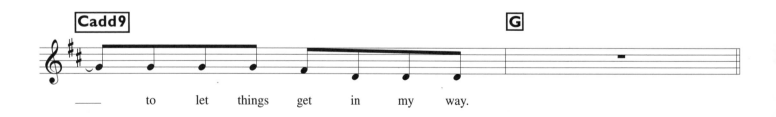

to let things get in my way.

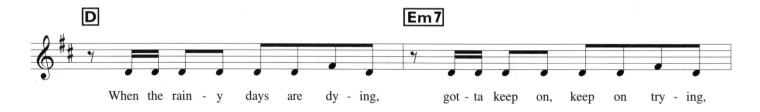

When the rain - y days are dy - ing, got - ta keep on, keep on try - ing,

all the bees and birds are fly - ing, ah._____

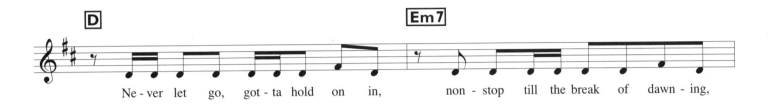

Ne - ver let go, got - ta hold on in, non - stop till the break of dawn - ing,

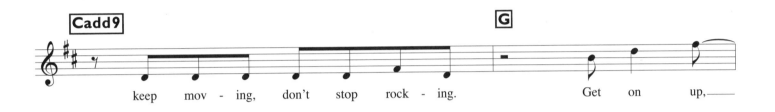

keep mov - ing, don't stop rock - ing. Get on up,_____

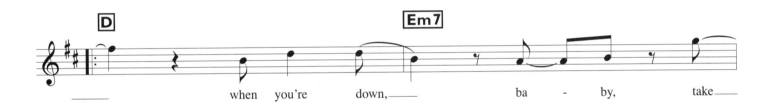

_____ when you're down,_____ ba - by, take_____

_____ a good look a - round._____ I know it's not

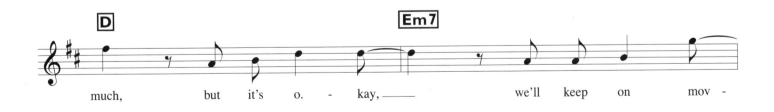

much, but it's o. - kay,_____ we'll keep on mov -

Repeat to fade

- ing on a - ny - way._____ Get on up_____

KIDS

Words & Music by Robbie Williams & Guy Chambers

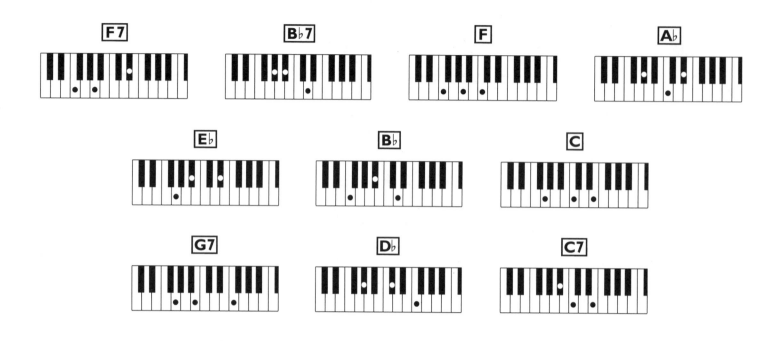

Voice: **Electric Piano 2**

Rhythm: **Funky Pop 1**

Tempo: ♩ = **92**

Ooh._____ Me no bub - bl - e - tious, me smoke hea - vy tar,

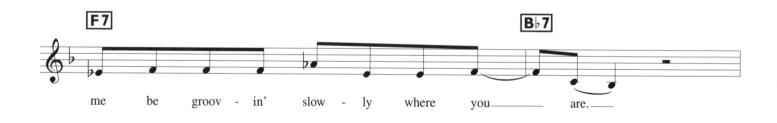

me be groov - in' slow - ly where you_____ are._____

No - ti - fy_____ your next_____ of kin, 'cause you're nev - er com - ing back,

I've been drop - ping beats ___ since Back in ___ Black. ___ And we'll

paint by num - bers till some - thing sticks, ___ I don't mind do - in' it for the kids. ___

___ (So come on.) Jump on board, take a ride, ___

___ yeah. ___ (You'll be doin' it alright.) Jump on

board, feel the high, ___ yeah, ___ 'cause the kids are al - right.

I like to drink it up but never like to sink it, uh, uh.   I like to drink it up but never like to sink it, uh, uh.

Repeat to fade

I like to drink it up but never like to sink it, uh, uh.   Uh uh uh, uh uh uh, uh uh uh, uh uh uh.

LIFT ME UP

Words & Music by Geri Halliwell, Andy Watkins,
Paul Wilson & Tracy Ackerman
© Copyright 1999 19 Music Limited/BMG Music Publishing Limited /
EMI Music Publishing (WP) Limited / Chrysalis Music Limited.
All Rights Reserved. International Copyright Secured.

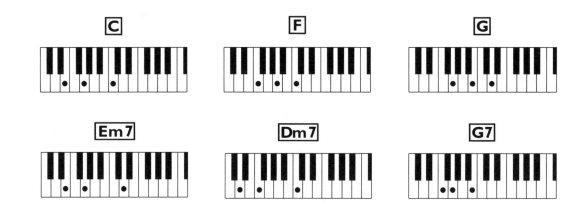

Voice: **Harp**

Rhythm: **New Age**

Tempo: ♩ = 108

Watch the first light— kiss the new world,—

it's a won - der— ba - by like you— and I.

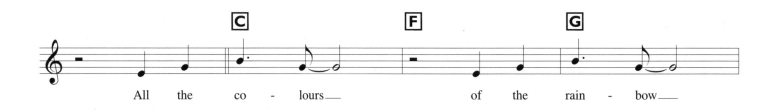

All the co - lours— of the rain - bow—

go - ing some - where,— ba - by like you— and I.

A LITTLE RESPECT

Words & Music by Vince Clarke & Andy Bell
© Copyright 1988 Musical Moments Limited/Minotaur Music Limited.
Sony/ATV Music Publishing (UK) Limited.
All Rights Reserved. International Copyright Secured.

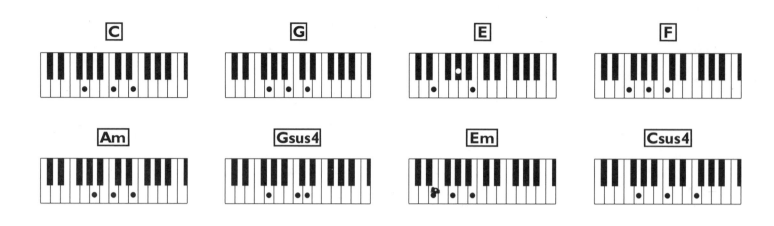

Voice: **Violin**

Rhythm: **8 Beat Pop**

Tempo: ♩ = 116

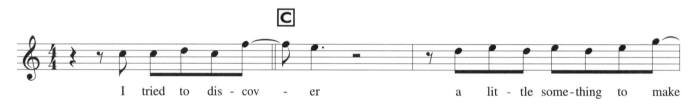

I tried to dis-cov — er a lit-tle some-thing to make

— me sweet — er, oh ba - by re - frain——

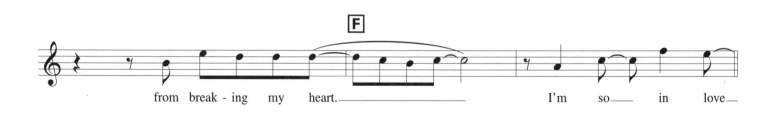

from break - ing my heart.———— I'm so—— in love

— with you,— I'll be— for - ev - er blue,—

that you give— me no rea - son, you know you're mak - ing me work so hard.—

That you give— me no, that you give— me no, that you give— me no, that you give— me no

soul.— I hear— you call - - - ing,—

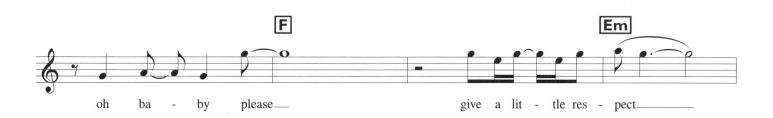

oh ba - by please— give a lit - tle res - pect

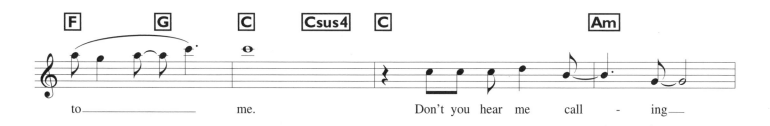

to— me. Don't you hear me call - ing—

oh ba - by please— give a lit - tle res - pect

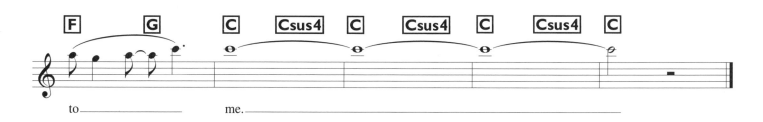

to— me.—

MR WRITER

Words & Music by Kelly Jones & Marshall Bird

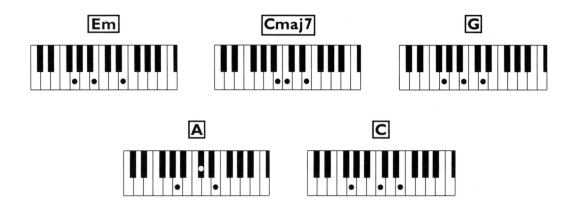

Voice: **Electric Guitar**

Rhythm: **Pop Ballad**

Tempo: ♩ = 80

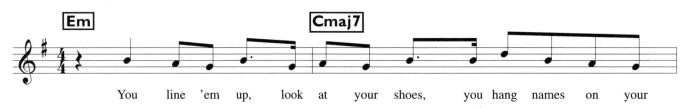

You line 'em up, look at your shoes, you hang names on your

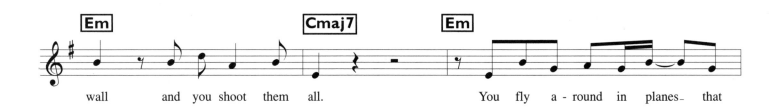

wall and you shoot them all. You fly a - round in planes that

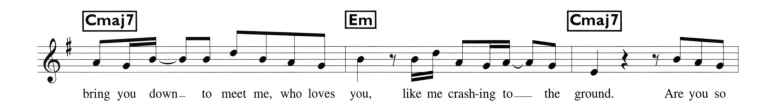

bring you down to meet me, who loves you, like me crash-ing to the ground. Are you so

lone - ly? You don't ev - en know me, but you'd like to stone me.

Mis - ter Writ - er, why don't you tell it like it is?

Why don't you tell it like it real - ly is

be-fore you go on home?

Mis - ter Wri - ter, why don't you tell it like it

real - ly is? Why don't you tell it like it

al - ways is be - fore you go on

Repeat to fade

home?

MY LOVE

Words & Music by Jörgen Elofsson, Pelle Nylén, David Kreuger & Per Magnusson

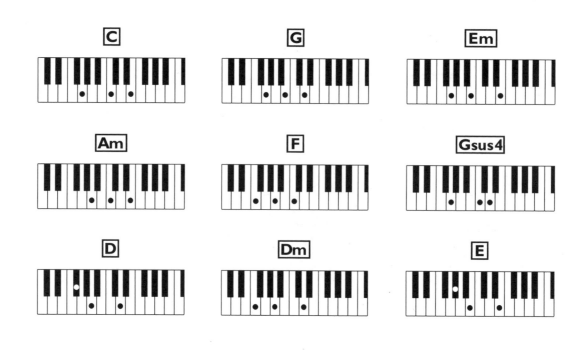

Voice: **Electric Guitar**

Rhythm: **Pop Ballad**

Tempo: ♩= 126

An emp-ty street, an emp-ty house, a hole in-side my heart. I'm all a-lone, the rooms are get-ting smal-ler. I won-der how, I won-der why, I won-der where they are, the days we had, the songs we sang to-geth-er, oh,—yeah. And oh my love, I'm hold-ing on for-ev-er, reach-ing for a love that seems so far So I

NO MATTER WHAT

Music by Andrew Lloyd Webber
Words by Jim Steinman

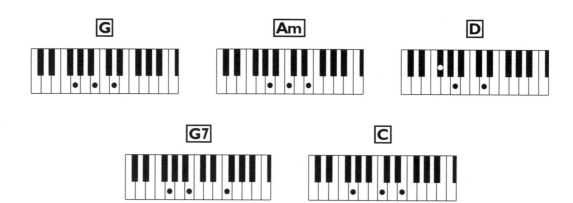

Voice: **Piano**

Rhythm: **Pop Rock I**

Tempo: ♩ = 84

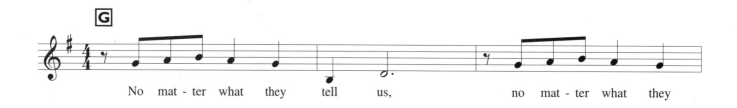

No mat-ter what they tell us, no mat-ter what they

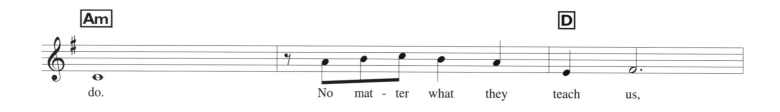

do. No mat-ter what they teach us,

what we be-lieve is true. No mat-ter what they

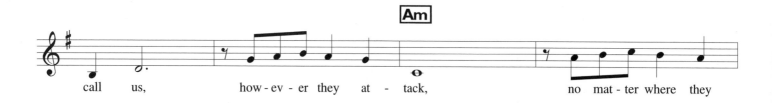

call us, how-ev-er they at-tack, no mat-ter where they

take us,   we'll find our own way back.____   I

can't de - ny____ what I____ be - lieve,____   I can't be____ what I'm not,____

____   I know our love's for - ev - er,

I know no mat - ter what.____   I can't de - ny____ what I____

____ be - lieve,____   I can't be____ what I'm not,____

I know our love's for - ev - er,   that's all that mat - ters now, no mat - ter

Repeat to fade

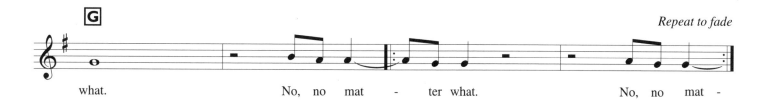

what.   No, no mat - ter what.   No, no mat -

NOBODY WANTS TO BE LONELY

Words & Music by Desmond Child, Victoria Shaw & Gary Burr

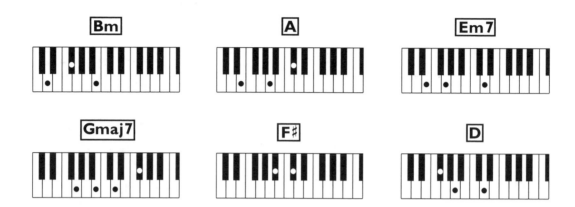

Voice: **Trumpet**

Rhythm: **Club Pop**

Tempo: ♩ = 104

Why,_____ why,_____ why._____

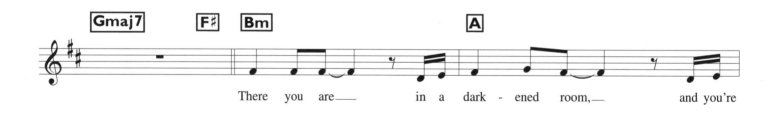

There you are___ in a dark-ened room,___ and you're

all a-lone___ look-ing out the win-dow, your heart is cold and lost

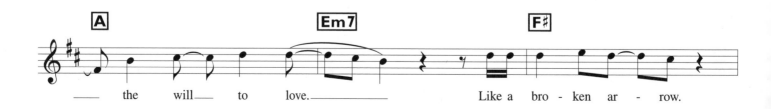

___ the will___ to love._____ Like a bro-ken ar-row.

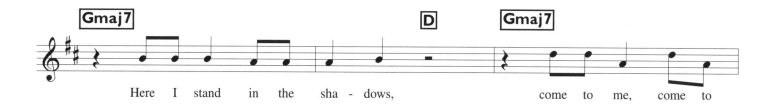

Here I stand in the sha - dows, come to me, come to

me, can't you see that no - bo - dy wants— to be lone - ly.

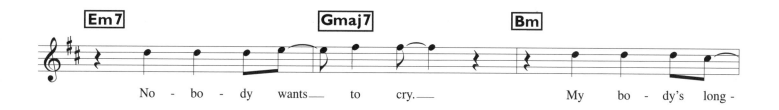

No - bo - dy wants— to cry.— My bo - dy's long -

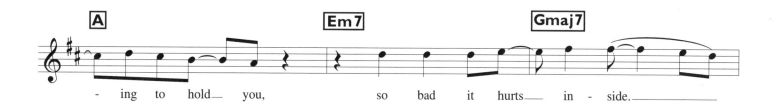

- ing to hold— you, so bad it hurts— in - side.—

Time is pre-cious and it's slip-ping a - way,— and I've been wait-ing for you all of my

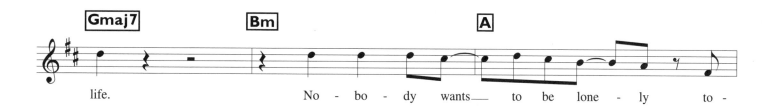

life. No - bo - dy wants— to be lone - ly to -

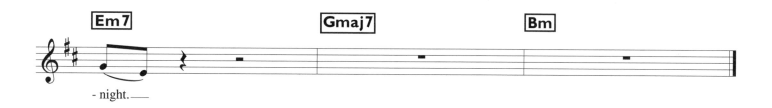

- night.—

ONE FOR SORROW

Words & Music by Mark Topham, Karl Twigg & Lance Ellington

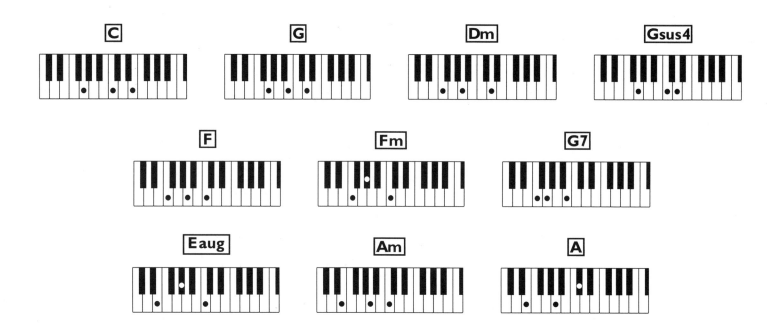

Voice: **Gut Guitar**

Rhythm: **Folky Pop**

Tempo: ♩ = 128

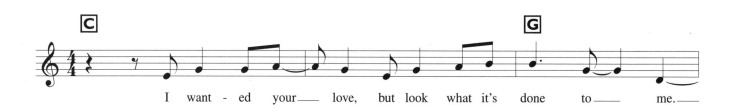

I want-ed your love, but look what it's done to me.

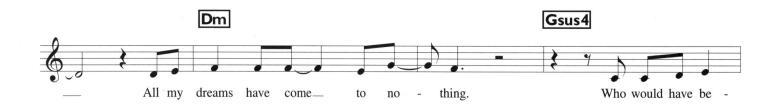

All my dreams have come to no-thing. Who would have be-

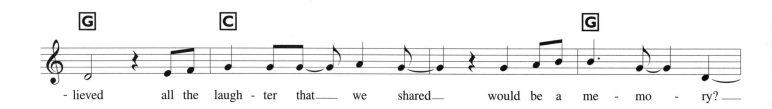

- lieved all the laugh-ter that we shared would be a me-mo-ry?

I can - not count the tears you've caused me,   if I could have

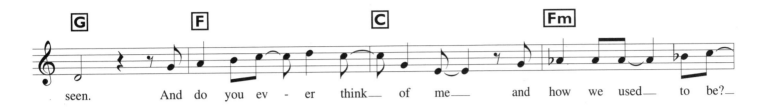

seen. And do you ev - er think of me   and how we used to be?

Oh, I know you're some - where else right now   and

lov - ing some - one else no doubt. Well I'm one   for sor - row, ain't it

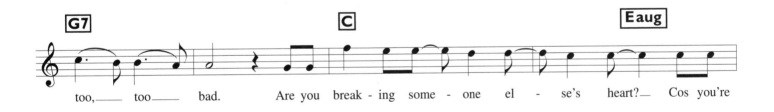

too, too bad.   Are you break - ing some - one el - se's heart? Cos you're

tak - ing my love where you are. Well I'm one   for sor - row, ain't it

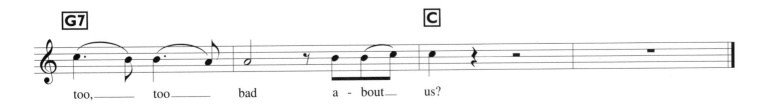

too, too bad a - bout us?

OOPS!... I DID IT AGAIN

Words & Music by Max Martin & Rami

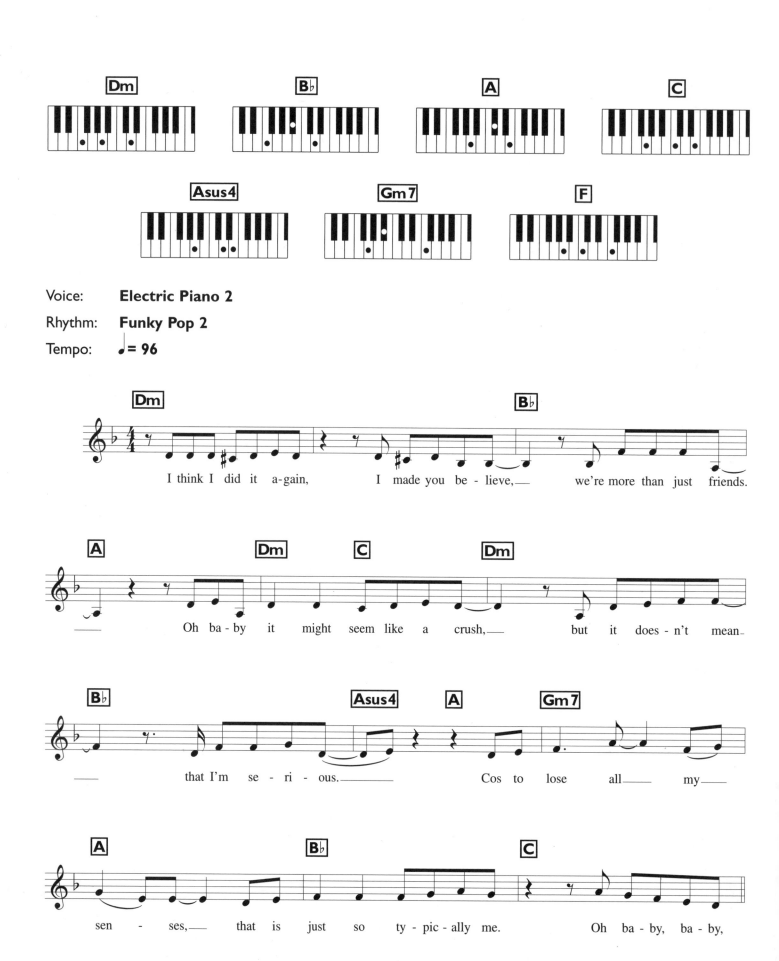

Voice: **Electric Piano 2**

Rhythm: **Funky Pop 2**

Tempo: ♩ = 96

OUT OF REACH

Words & Music by Gabrielle & Jonathan Shorten

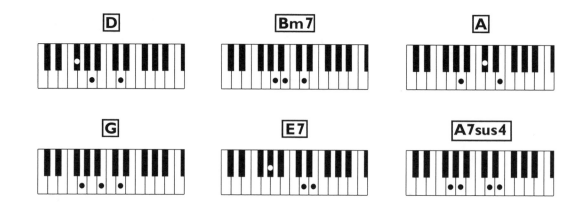

Voice: **Soprano Saxophone**

Rhythm: **Pop Ballad**

Tempo: ♩ **= 92**

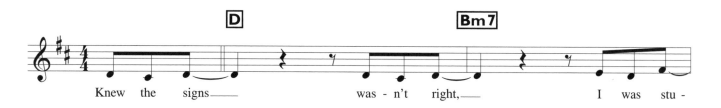

Knew the signs____ was - n't right,____ I was stu -

- pid for a while,____ swept a - way____ by____ you____

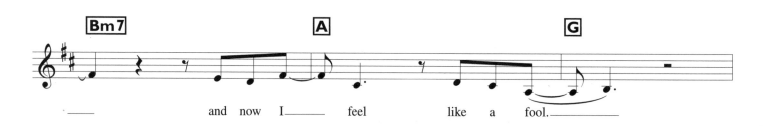

____ and now I____ feel like a fool.____

So con - fused, my heart's____ bruised.

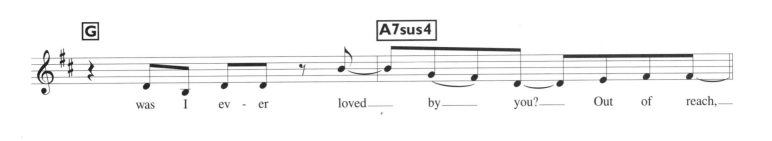

PRAISE YOU

Words & Music by Norman Cook & Camille Yarborough
© Copyright 1998 Maat Music Company/
Vogue Music/PolyGram Music Publishing Limited.
Universal Music Publishing Limited.

Voice: **Piano 1**

Rhythm: **Disco**

Tempo: ♩ = 108

We've come a long, long way to-geth-er through the

hard times___ and the good.___ I have to ce-le-brate you ba-

- by, I have to praise you like I should.___

___ I have to praise you, I have to

PURE AND SIMPLE

Words & Music by Tim Hawes, Pete Kirtley & Alison Clarkson

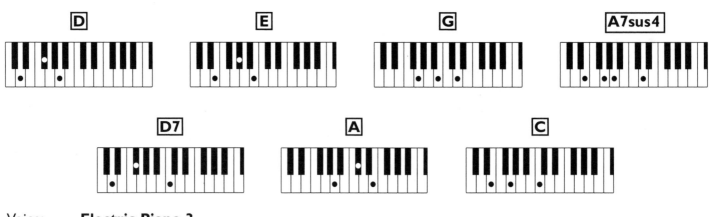

Voice: **Electric Piano 3**

Rhythm: **Pop Rock 1**

Tempo: ♩ = **76**

You been saying I'm driving you crazy   and I haven't been around for you lately,   but I had a few things on my mind.

When I'm with you I am filled with e-mo-tion,   can't you see that I'm giv-ing you de-vo-tion,

and a love like this is hard to find.___   I know I've been a' walk-ing a-round_ in a   daze,

___ ba-by, ba-by.   You got-ta be-lieve_ me_ when_ I_ say___   wher-ev-er you

go,   what-ev-er you do,   it's pure and sim - ple,—   I'll be there— for you.—   What-ev-er it

takes,   I swear it's true,—   it's pure and sim - ple,—   I'll be there— for you.—

I'll al-ways be there— for you ba - by,   you know that I'll al - ways be— a - round,—   oh yeah.

—   I'll al-ways be there— for you ho - ney,   you know I nev-er let— you

down,   'cause you're the on - ly one   for me.   Wher-ev- er you

go,   what-ev-er you do,   it's pure and sim - ple,—   I'll be there— for you.—   What-ev-er it

takes,   I swear it's true,—   it's pure and sim - ple,—   I'll be there— for you.—   Wher-ev-er you

Repeat to fade

RISE

Words & Music by Bob Dylan, Gabrielle,
Ferdy Unger-Hamilton & Ollie Dagois
© Copyright 1999 Ram's Horn Music, USA /
Perfect Songs Limited / Chrysalis Music Limited.
All Rights Reserved. International Copyright Secured.

Voice: **Clarinet**

Rhythm: **Soul Ballad**

Tempo: ♩ = 72

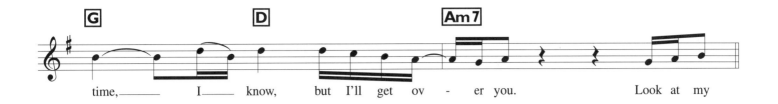

time,_____ I_____ know, but I'll get ov - er you. Look at my

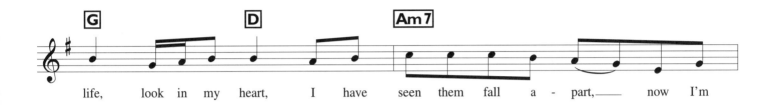

life, look in my heart, I have seen them fall a - part,_____ now I'm

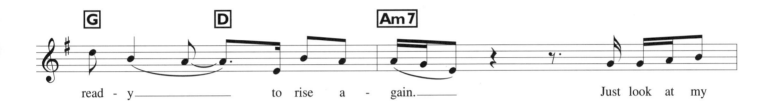

read - y_____ to rise a - gain._____ Just look at my

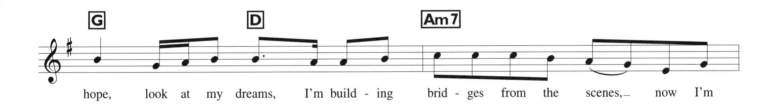

hope, look at my dreams, I'm build - ing brid - ges from the scenes,_ now I'm

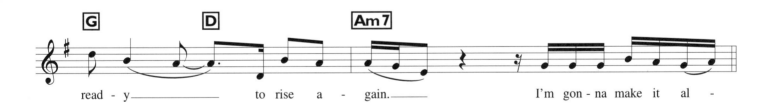

read - y_____ to rise a - gain._____ I'm gon - na make it al -

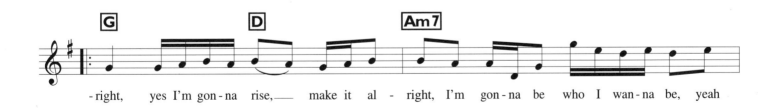

-right, yes I'm gon - na rise,_____ make it al - right, I'm gon - na be who I wan - na be, yeah

Repeat to fade

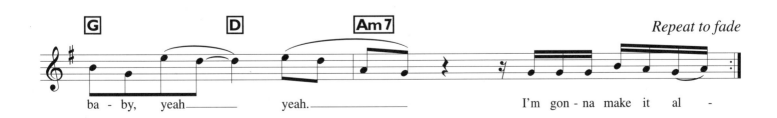

ba - by, yeah_____ yeah._____ I'm gon - na make it al -

THE ROAD TO MANDALAY

Words & Music by Robbie Williams & Guy Chambers
© Copyright 2000 EMI Virgin Music Limited / BMG Music Publishing Limited.
All Rights Reserved. International Copyright Secured.

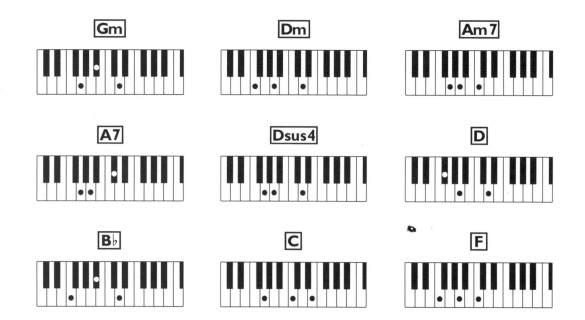

Voice: **Mute Guitar**

Rhythm: **Soft Rock**

Tempo: ♩ = 100

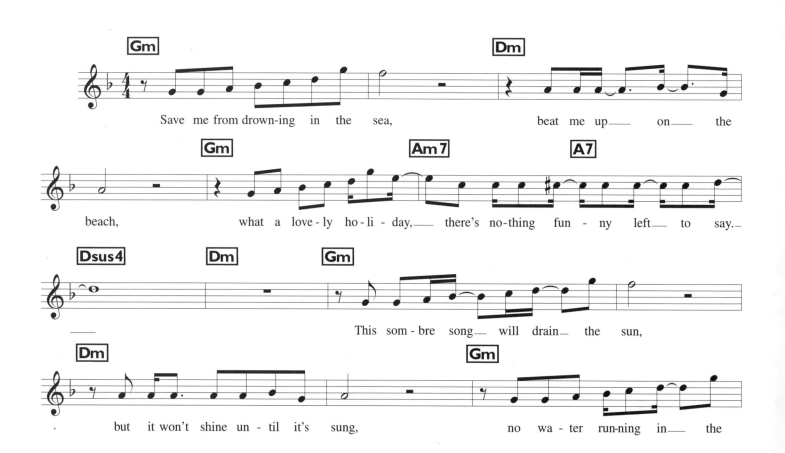

Save me from drown-ing in the sea, beat me up on the beach, what a love-ly ho-li-day, there's no-thing fun-ny left to say.

This som-bre song will drain the sun, but it won't shine un-til it's sung, no wa-ter run-ning in the

RUN FOR COVER

Words & Music by Cameron McVey, Johnny Lipsey,
Paul Simm, Siobhan Donaghy, Keisha Buchanan & Mutya Buena

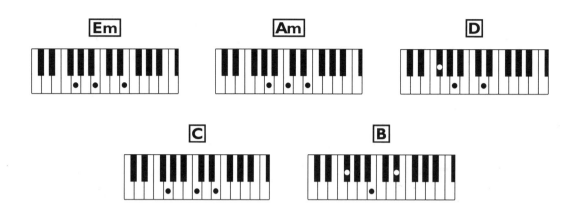

Voice: **Studio Piano**

Rhythm: **Groove Soul**

Tempo: ♩ = 108

When blues————— get me down—————

then I————— get turned a -

- round————— I tend to—————

cut my - self off—————

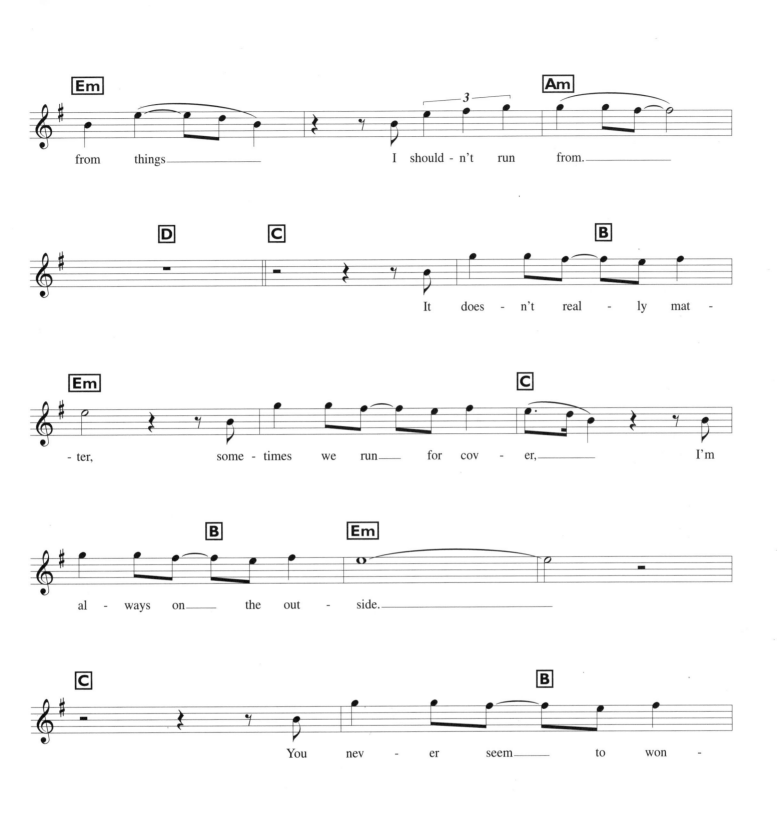

from things_____ I should-n't run from._____

It does-n't real-ly mat-

-ter, some-times we run___ for cov-er,_____ I'm

al-ways on___ the out-side._____

You nev-er seem___ to won-

-der how much you make___ me suf-fer,_____ I

speak it from___ the in-side._____

SHINING LIGHT

Words & Music by Tim Wheeler

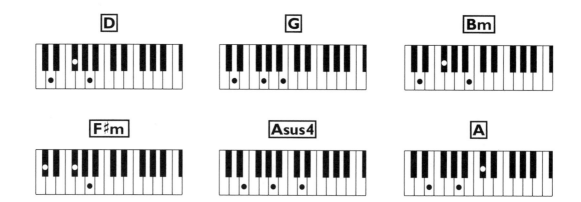

Voice: **Piano**

Rhythm: **Pop Rock 2**

Tempo: ♩ = 104

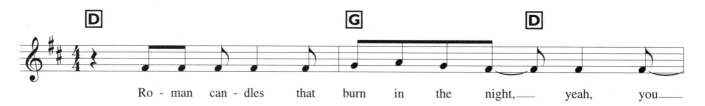

Ro - man can - dles that burn in the night,___ yeah, you___

___ are a shin - ing light.___ You lit a torch in the

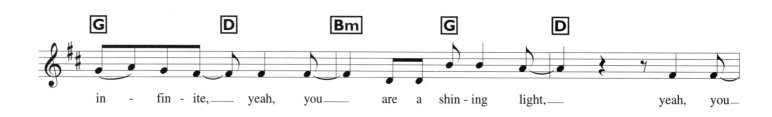

in - fin - ite,___ yeah, you___ are a shin - ing light,___ yeah, you___

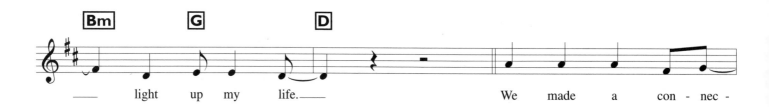

___ light up my life.___ We made a con - nec -

SHOW ME THE MEANING OF BEING LONELY

Words by Herbert Crichlow
Music by Max Martin

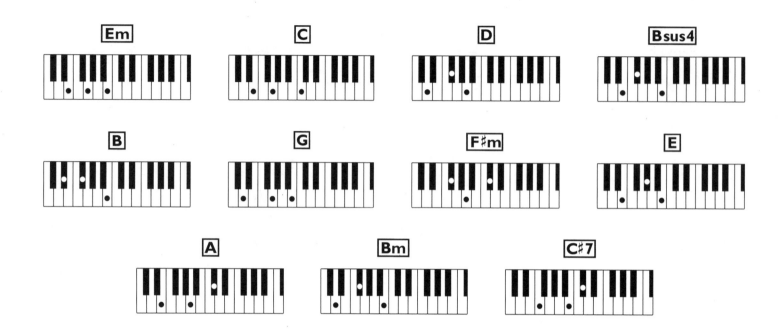

Voice: **Piano 2**

Rhythm: **Pop Ballad**

Tempo: ♩ = **85**

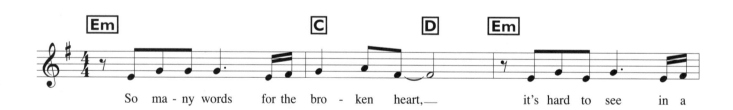

So ma-ny words for the bro-ken heart,— it's hard to see in a

crim-son love,— so hard to breathe.— Walk with me — and may-be nights of light so

soon be-come— wild and free, I could feel the sun.— Your ev-'ry wish—

will be done,— they tell me. Show me the mean-ing of be-ing lone-ly. Is this the feel-ing I

need to walk— with? Tell me why I can't be there— where you are,———— there's

some-thing miss-ing in my heart. There's no-where to run,— I have no— place to go.— Sur-ren-der my heart,—

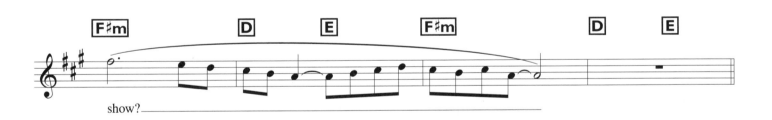

—— bo - dy and soul.— How can it be, you're ask - ing me to feel— the things you ne - ver

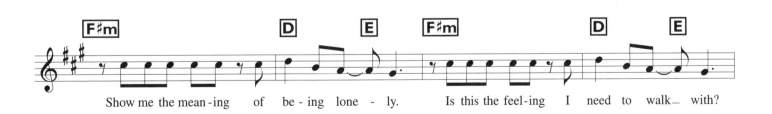

show?————————

Show me the mean-ing of be-ing lone - ly. Is this the feel-ing I need to walk— with?

Tell me why I can't be there— where you are,———— there's some-thing miss-ing in my heart.

SING

Words & Music by Fran Healy
© Copyright 2001 Sony/ATV Music Publishing (UK) Limited.
All Rights Reserved. International Copyright Secured.

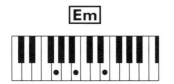

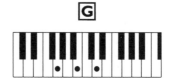
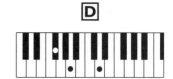

Voice: **Acoustic Guitar**

Rhythm: **Funky Pop 2**

Tempo: ♩ = 80

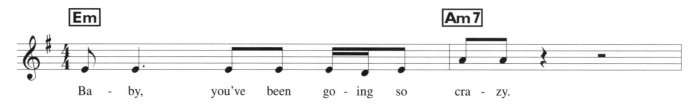

Ba - by, you've been go - ing so cra - zy.

Late - ly noth - ing seems to be go - ing right.

So a - lone, oh why d'ya have to get so a - lone?

You're sore, you've been wait - in' in the sun too long. But if you

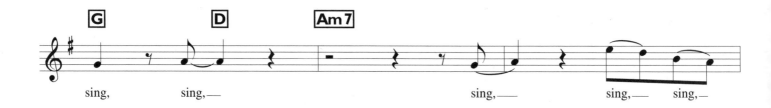

sing, sing, sing, sing, sing,

SING IT BACK

Words & Music by Mark Brydon & Roisin Murphy

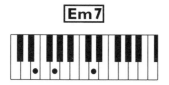 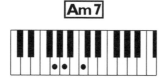 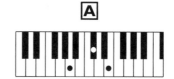 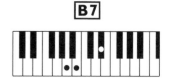

Voice: **Bass/Gut Guitar Split**

Rhythm: **Club Pop**

Tempo: ♩ = 124

When you are rea-dy, I will sur-ren-der, take me and do as you

wish. Have what you want, your way's al-ways the best way.

I have suc-cumbed to this pas-sive sen-sa-tion,

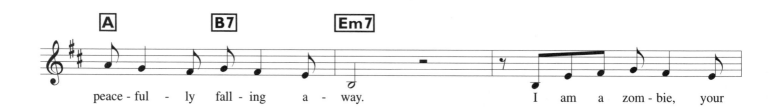

peace-ful-ly fall-ing a-way. I am a zom-bie, your

wish will com-mand me, laugh as I fall to my knees.

Bring it back, sing it back, bring it back,

sing it back to me.___ Bring it back, sing it back,

bring it back, sing it back to me.___ Come, come,

come to my sweet me - lo - dy.___ Come, come,

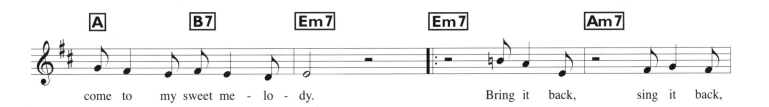

come to my sweet me - lo - dy. Bring it back, sing it back,

bring it back, sing it back to me.___ Bring it back,

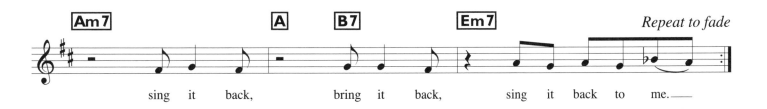

Repeat to fade

sing it back, bring it back, sing it back to me.___

SO WHY SO SAD

Words & Music by James Dean Bradfield, Nicky Wire & Sean Moore

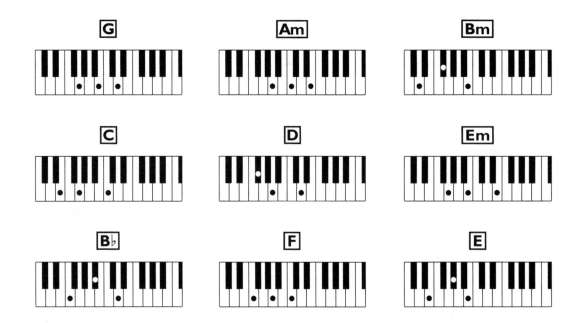

Voice:	**Distortion Guitar**
Rhythm:	**8 Beat Pop**
Tempo:	♩ = 124

Things get clear_____ when I feel free,_____

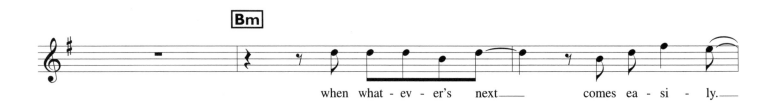

when what - ev - er's next_____ comes ea - si - ly.

_____ When gen - tle hands_____

give life to me,_____ when your eyes_____

fill with_ ti - ny tears._____

So why, so sad?_____ You live and you love._____

So why, so sad?_____ De - pen-dent on_____ a - bove._____

Search-ing for_____ the dead sea scrolls._____ So

why, so_____ why, so sad? So

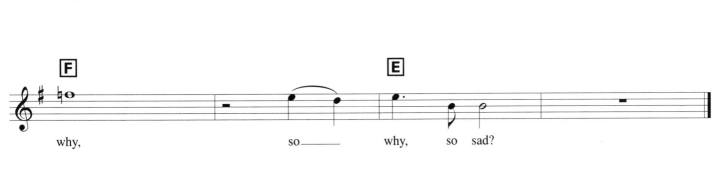

why, so_____ why, so sad?

STRONGER

Words & Music by Max Martin & Rami

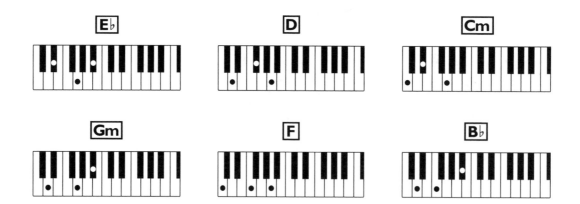

Voice: **Brass Ensemble**

Rhythm: **Funky Pop 1**

Tempo: ♩ = 108

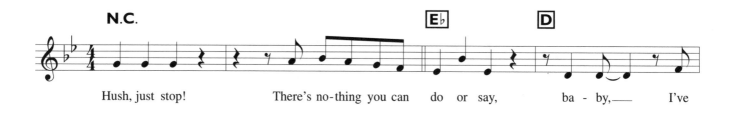

Hush, just stop! There's no-thing you can do or say, ba - by,__ I've

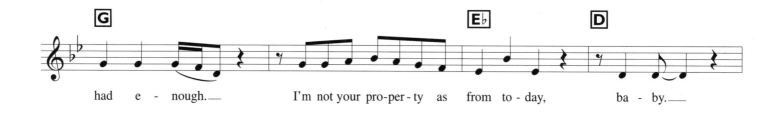

had e - nough.__ I'm not your pro-per-ty as from to - day, ba - by.__

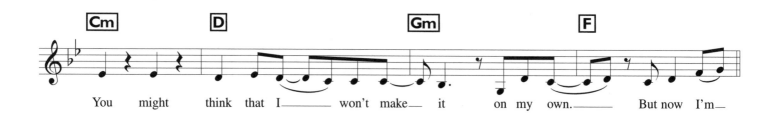

You might think that I__ won't make__ it on my own.__ But now I'm__

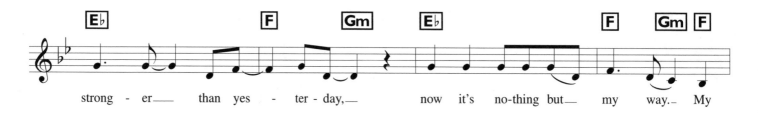

strong - er__ than yes - ter - day,__ now it's no-thing but__ my way.__ My

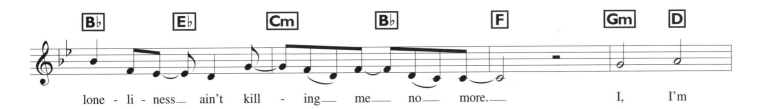

lone - li - ness— ain't kill - ing— me— no— more.— I, I'm

strong - er,— oh c - 'mon— now, oh yeah.—

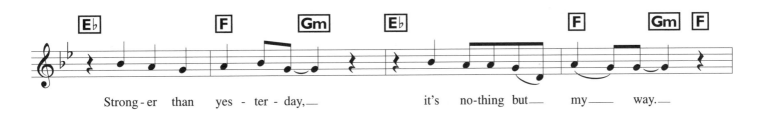

Strong - er than yes - ter - day,— it's no-thing but— my— way.—

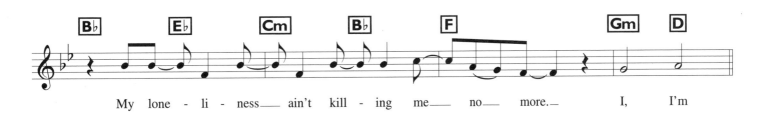

My lone - li - ness— ain't kill - ing me— no— more.— I, I'm

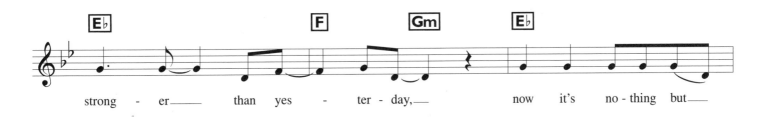

strong - er— than yes - ter - day,— now it's no-thing but—

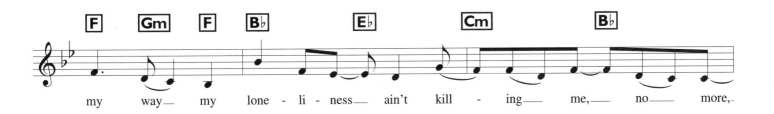

my way— my lone - li - ness— ain't kill - ing— me,— no— more,-

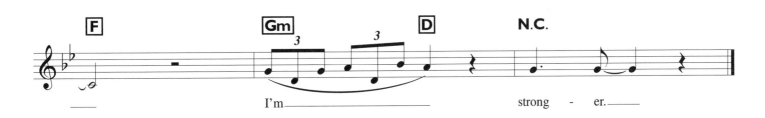

I'm— strong - er.—

71

SUPREME

Words & Music by Robbie Williams, Guy Chambers,
Dino Fekaris, Frederick Perren & Francois de Roubaix

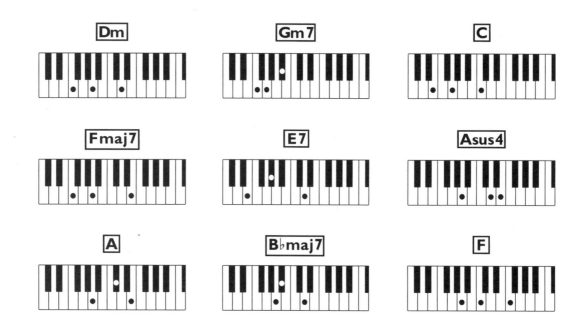

Voice: **Piano 1**

Rhythm: **Lite Pop**

Tempo: ♩ = 120

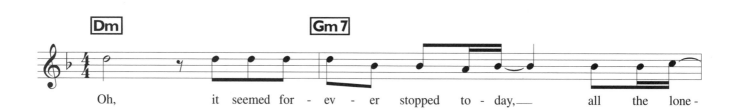

Oh, it seemed for - ev - er stopped to - day,___ all the lone -

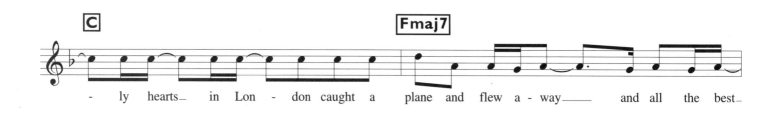

- ly hearts___ in Lon - don caught a plane and flew a - way___ and all the best

___ wo - man___ are mar - ried,___ all the hand - some men are gay,___ you feel de - prived.

Yeah, are you ques-tion-ing your size, is there a tu-mour in your hu-mour, are there bags

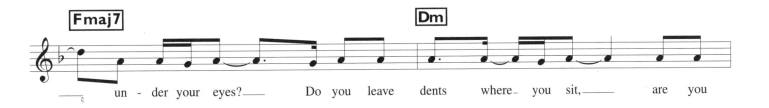

un - der your eyes? Do you leave dents where you sit, are you

get-ting on a bit, will you sur - vive? You must sur - vive. When there's no

love in town, this new cen-tu - ry keeps bring-ing you down,

all the pla - ces you have been try - ing to find

a love su - preme, a love su-preme. Come and live a love su - preme,

Repeat to fade

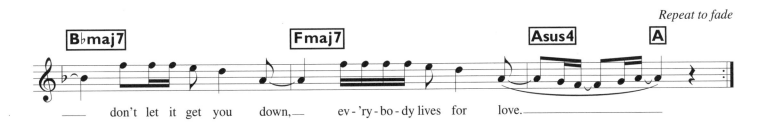

don't let it get you down, ev-'ry-bo-dy lives for love.

SURVIVOR

Words & Music by Beyoncé Knowles, Anthony Dent & Matthew Knowles
© Copyright 2001 Beyoncé Publishing/Sony/ATV Tunes LLC/Hitco
South/Chase Muzic Incorporated/Music Of Windswept, USA.
Windswept Music (London) Limited /
Sony/ATV Music Publishing (UK) Limited / Copyright Control.
All Rights Reserved. International Copyright Secured.

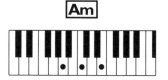
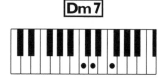
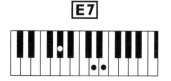
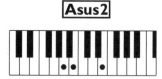

Voice: **Electric Guitar**

Rhythm: **Pop Ballad**

Tempo: ♩ = 80

Now that you're out-ta my life I'm so much bet-ter, you thought that I'd be

weak with-out you, but I'm strong-er. You thought that I'd be

broke with-out you, but I'm rich-er, you thought that I'd be

sad with out you, I laugh hard-er. Thought I would-n't

grow with-out you, now I'm wis-er. Thought that I'd be

help - less with - out_____ you, but I'm smart - er. You thought that I'd be

stressed with - out_____ you but I'm chill - in'. You thought I would - n't

sell with - out_____ you, sold nine mil - lion. I'm a sur -

- vi - vor, I'm not gon' give up, I'm not gon' stop, (what) I'm gon' work hard - er, I'm a sur -

- vi - vor. I'm gon - na make it, I will sur - vive, (what) keep on sur - vi - vin', I'm a sur -

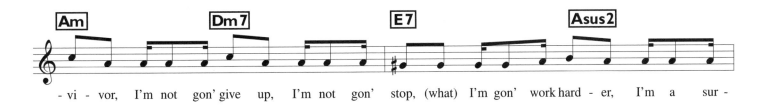

- vi - vor, I'm not gon' give up, I'm not gon' stop, (what) I'm gon' work hard - er, I'm a sur -

- vi - vor, I'm gon - na make it, I will sur - vive, (what) keep on sur - vi - vin'.

THAT DON'T IMPRESS ME MUCH

Words & Music by Shania Twain & R.J. Lange

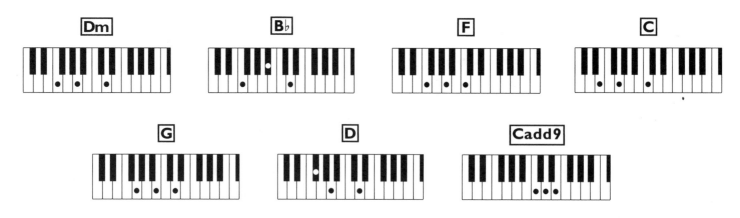

Voice: **Slap Bass**

Rhythm: **8 Beat Pop**

Tempo: ♩ = 110

I've known a few guys who thought they were pret-ty smart,— but

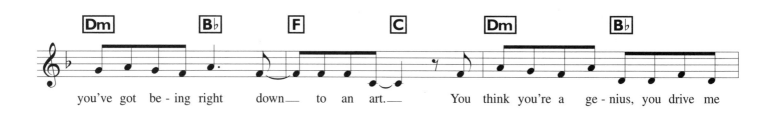

you've got be-ing right down— to an art.— You think you're a ge-nius, you drive me

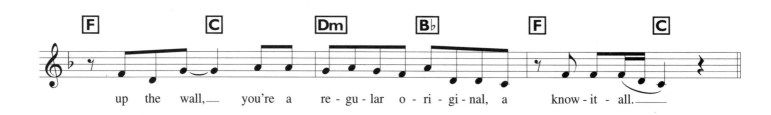

up the wall,— you're a re-gu-lar o-ri-gi-nal, a know-it-all.——

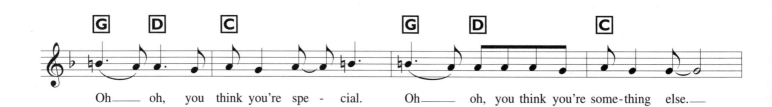

Oh—— oh, you think you're spe-cial. Oh—— oh, you think you're some-thing else.——

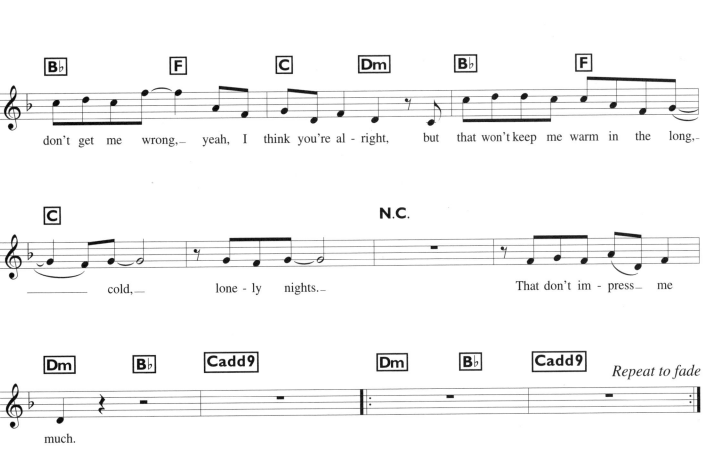

THIS YEAR'S LOVE

Words & Music by David Gray

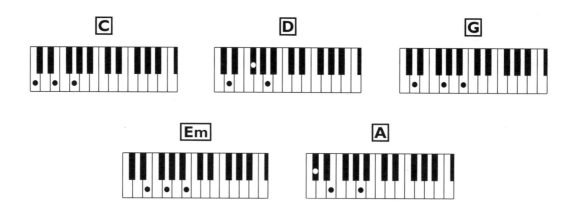

Voice: **Studio Piano**

Rhythm: **Love Ballad**

Tempo: ♩. = 54

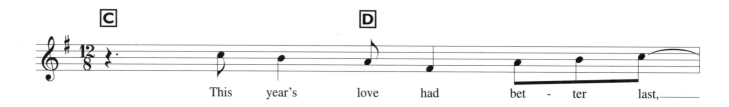

This year's love had bet - ter last,

hea - ven knows, it's high

time. I've been wait - ing on my own too— long.—

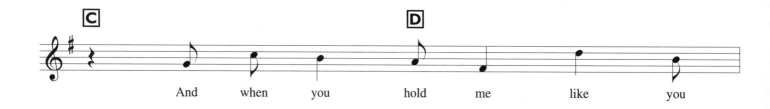

And when you hold me like you

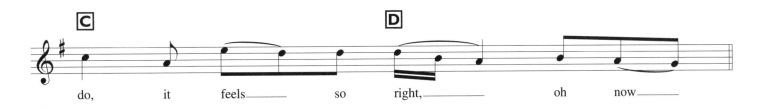

do, it feels_____ so right,_____ oh now_____

be - fore I op - en up my arms and fall, los - ing

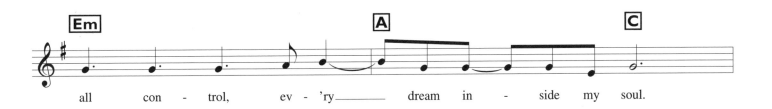

all con - trol, ev - 'ry_____ dream in - side my soul.

When you kiss me on that mid - night street, sweep me

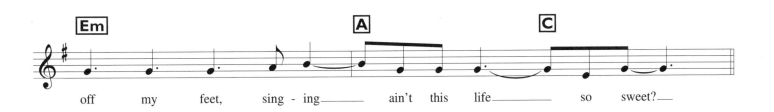

off my feet, sing - ing_____ ain't this life_____ so sweet?_____

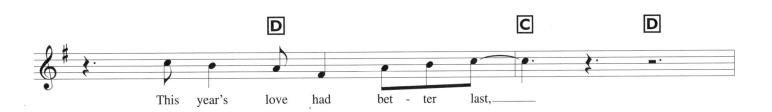

This year's love had bet - ter last,_____

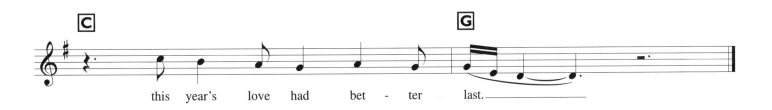

this year's love had bet - ter last._____

TROUBLE

Words & Music by Guy Berryman, Jon Buckland,
Will Champion & Chris Martin

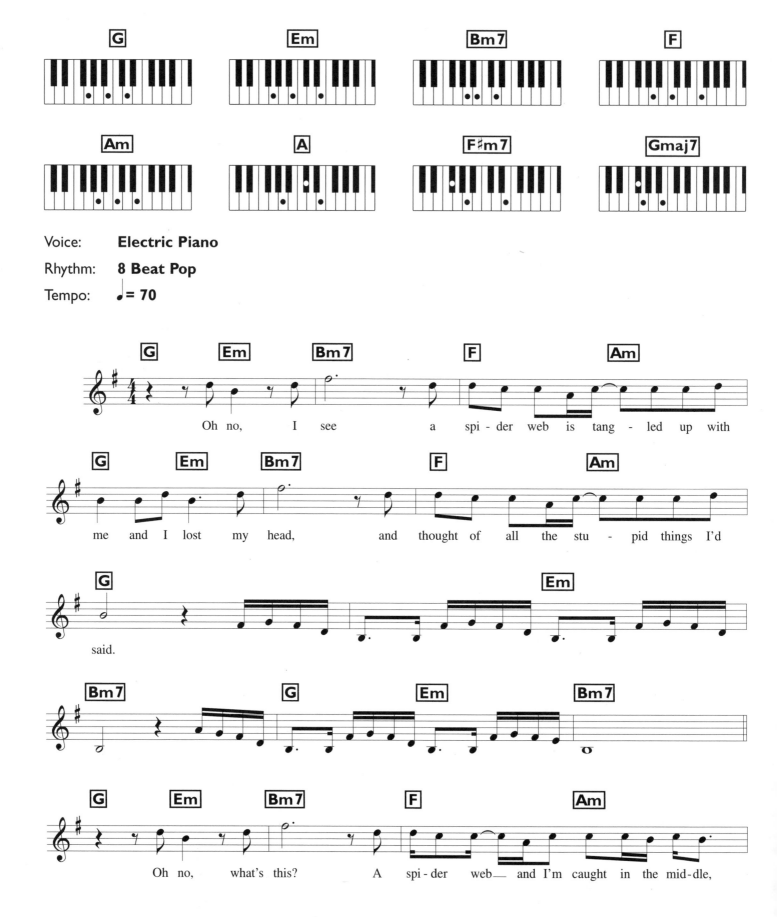

Voice: **Electric Piano**

Rhythm: **8 Beat Pop**

Tempo: ♩ = 70

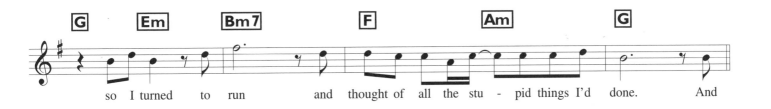

so I turned to run and thought of all the stu - pid things I'd done. And

ah,___ I nev-er meant to cause you trou-ble. And ah,___ I nev-er meant to do you

wrong. And ah,___ well if I ev - er caused you trou-ble, and

oh no, I nev - er meant to do you harm. They spun a

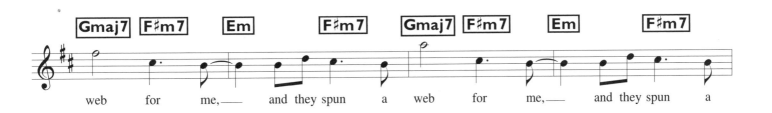

web for me,___ and they spun a web for me,___ and they spun a

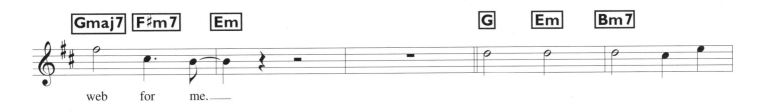

web for me.___

TURN

Words & Music by Fran Healy

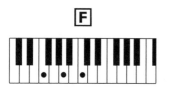 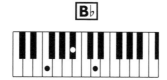 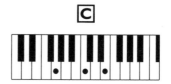 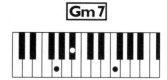

Voice: **Distortion Guitar**

Rhythm: **Straight Rock**

Tempo: ♩ = 74

I want to see what peo - ple saw,

I want to feel like I felt be - fore. I'd like to see

the king - dom come, I want to feel for - ev - er young.

I want to sing, to sing my song.

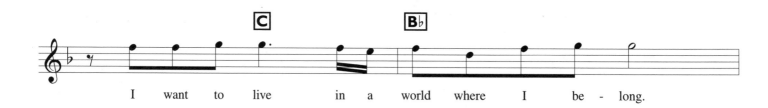

I want to live in a world where I be - long.

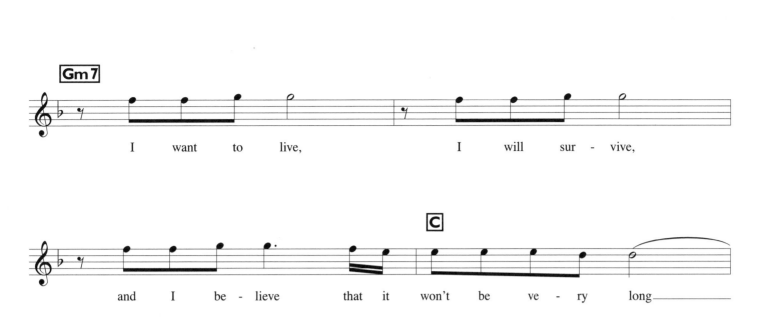

I want to live, I will sur - vive,

and I be - lieve that it won't be ve - ry long

if we turn, turn,

turn, turn, turn, turn, turn, turn.

If we turn, turn,

turn, turn, turn, we might learn, learn to

turn, oh hi.

WALKING AWAY

Words & Music by Craig David & Mark Hill
© Copyright 1999 Windswept Music (London) Limited /
Warner Chappell Music Limited.

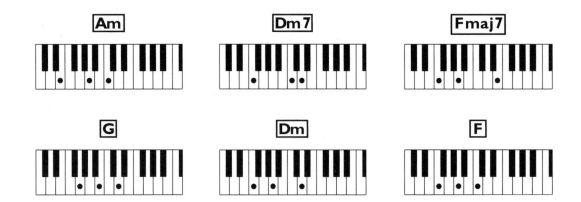

Voice: **Piano 2**

Rhythm: **16 Beat Pop**

Tempo: ♩ = **88**

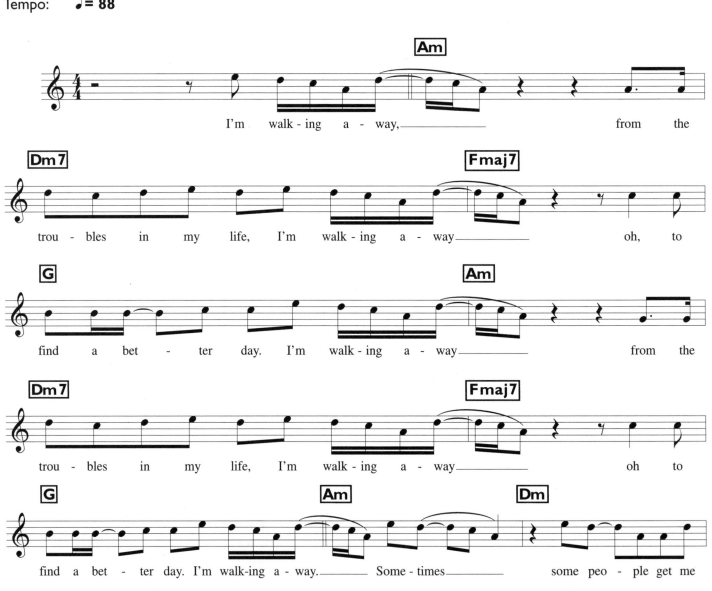

wrong,——— when it's some-thing I've said or done.— Some-times———

—— you feel—— there is no——— fun,——— that's why you turn and run.———

But now I tru - ly re - a - lise some peo - ple don't wan - na com - pro - mise.——

Well I saw them with my——— own eyes, spread - ing those lies——— and,

well I don't wan - na live—— my life,——— too ma - ny sleep - less nights——

not men - tion - ing—— the fights,——— I'm sor - ry to say—— la - dy, I'm walk - ing a - way——

from the trou - bles in my life, I'm walk - ing a - way——— oh, to

find a bet - ter day. I'm walk - ing a - way——— from the

Repeat to fade

trou - bles in my life, I'm walk-ing a - way——— oh to find a bet - ter day. I'm walk-ing a - way.—

WHAT IT FEELS LIKE FOR A GIRL

Words & Music by Madonna & Guy Sigsworth

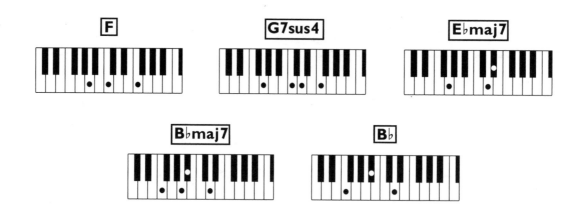

Voice: **Clarinet**

Rhythm: **Soul Ballad**

Tempo: ♩ = 104

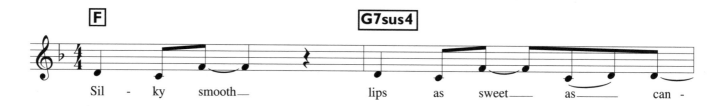

Sil - ky smooth___ lips as sweet___ as___ can -

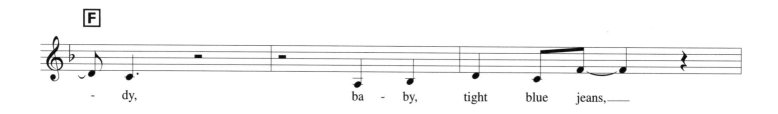

- dy, ba - by, tight blue jeans,___

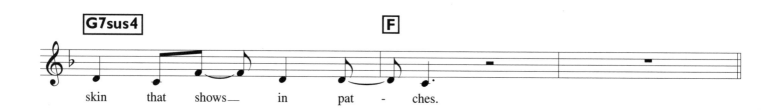

skin that shows___ in pat - ches.

Strong in - side___ but you don't know___ it,

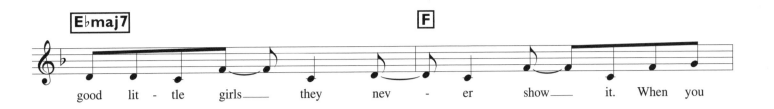

good lit - tle girls___ they nev - er show___ it. When you

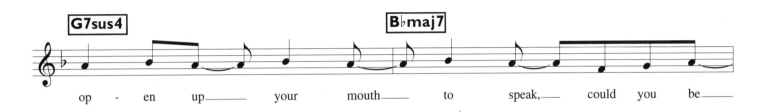

op - en up___ your mouth___ to speak,___ could you be___

___ a lit - tle weak?___ Do you know what it

feels like for a girl? Do you

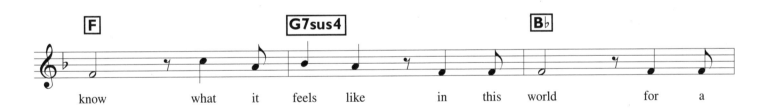

know what it feels like in this world for a

girl? Do you know what it feels like for a

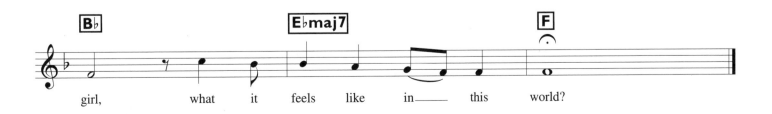

girl, what it feels like in___ this world?

WHAT MAKES A MAN

Words & Music by Steve Mac & Wayne Hector

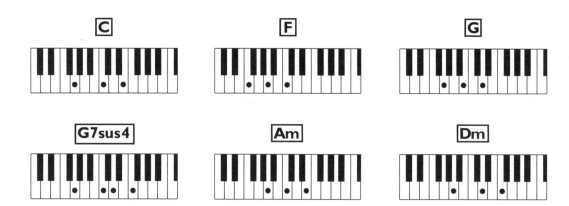

Voice: **Electric Piano 4**

Rhythm: **Pop Ballad**

Tempo: ♩ = 74

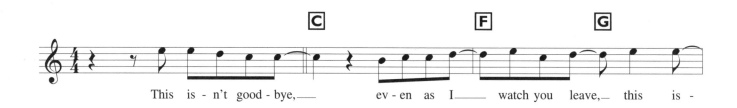

This is-n't good-bye,— ev-en as I— watch you leave,— this is-

-n't good-bye,— I swear I won't cry.— Ev-en as tears— fill my eyes,— I swear

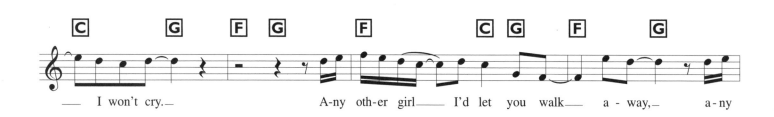

— I won't cry.— A-ny oth-er girl— I'd let you walk— a-way,— a-ny

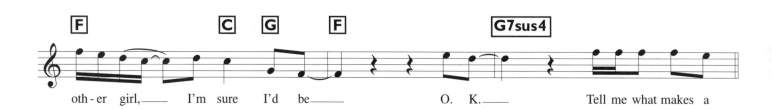

oth-er girl,— I'm sure I'd be— O. K.— Tell me what makes a

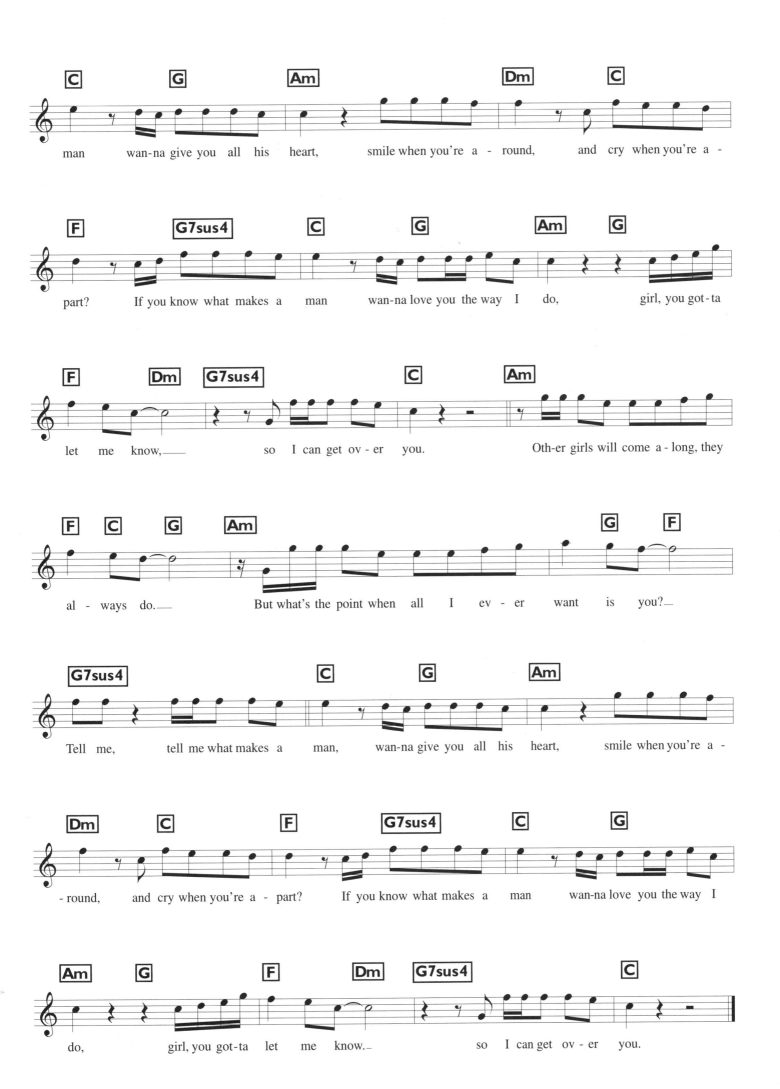

WHAT TOOK YOU SO LONG?

Words & Music by Emma Bunton, Richard Stannard, Julian Gallagher,
Martin Harrington, John Themis & Dave Morgan

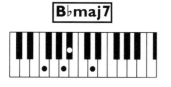 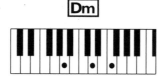 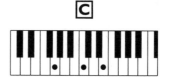 

Voice: **Piano 1**

Rhythm: **Lite Pop**

Tempo: ♩ = 120

Oh talk to me, can't you see,

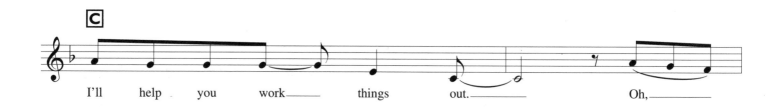

I'll help you work things out. Oh,

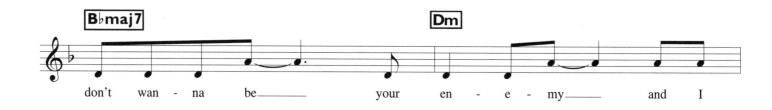

don't wan - na be your en - e - my and I

don't wan - na scream and shout 'cause ba - by

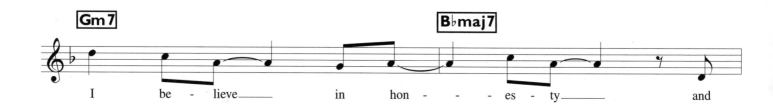

I be - lieve in hon - es - ty and

then be strong— and true.— I should-n't have— to say—

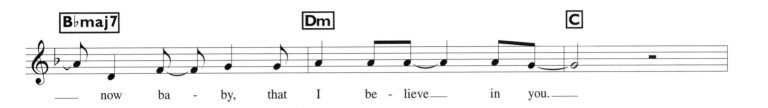

— now ba - by, that I be - lieve— in you.—

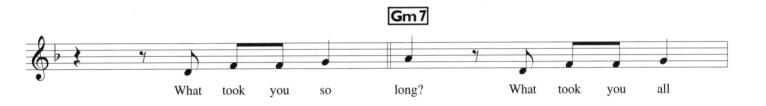

What took you so long? What took you all

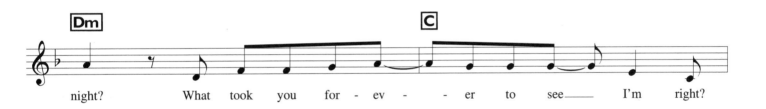

night? What took you for - ev - - er to see— I'm right?

You know I treat you so good, I make you feel fine, you know I'll nev -

- er give it up this time,— no,— no,— no.

WHEN YOU SAY NOTHING AT ALL

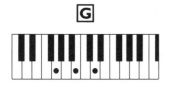
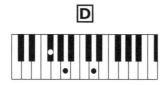
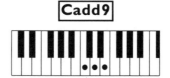
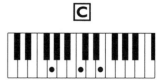

Voice: **Electric Piano 2**

Rhythm: **Pop Ballad**

Tempo: ♩ = 88

It's a-maz-ing how you can speak right to my heart

with-out say-ing a word,

you can light up the dark.

Try as I may, I can ne-ver ex-plain

what I hear when you don't say a thing.

The smile on your face____ lets me know____

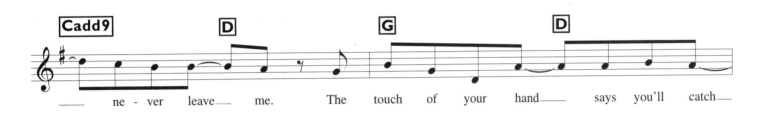

____ that you need____ me, there's a truth in your eyes____ say - ing you'll____

____ ne - ver leave____ me. The touch of your hand____ says you'll catch____

____ me wher - ev - er I fall.____

You say it best,____ when you say no - thing at all.____

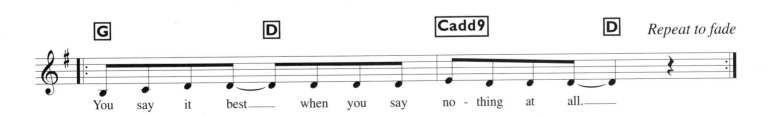

You say it best____ when you say no - thing at all.____

Repeat to fade

WHOLE AGAIN

Words & Music by Stuart Kershaw, Andy McCluskey, Bill Padley & Jeremy Godfrey

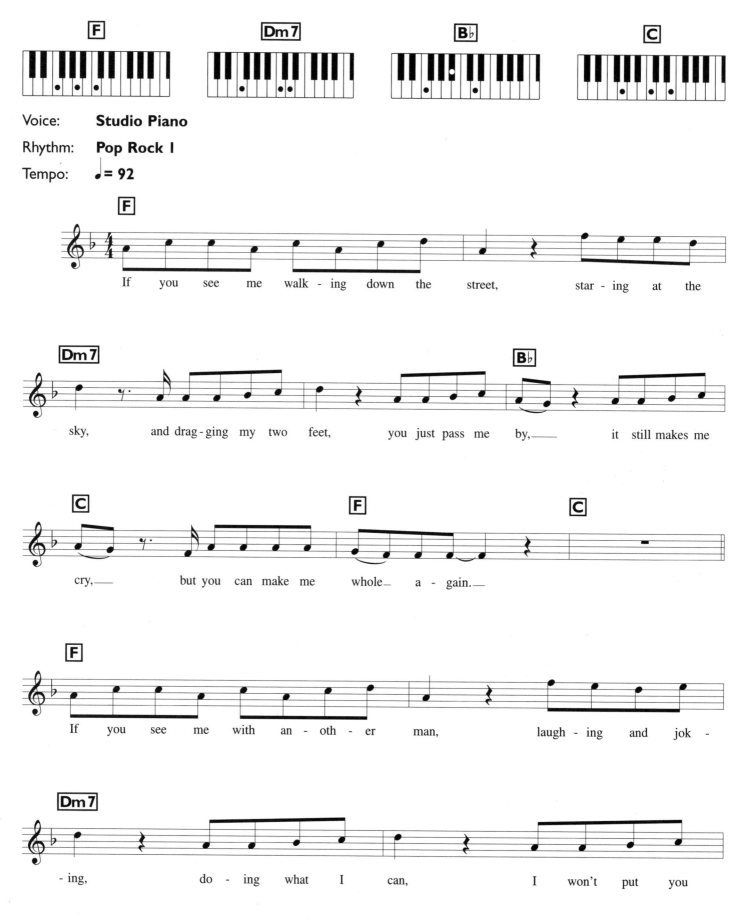

Voice: **Studio Piano**

Rhythm: **Pop Rock 1**

Tempo: ♩ = 92

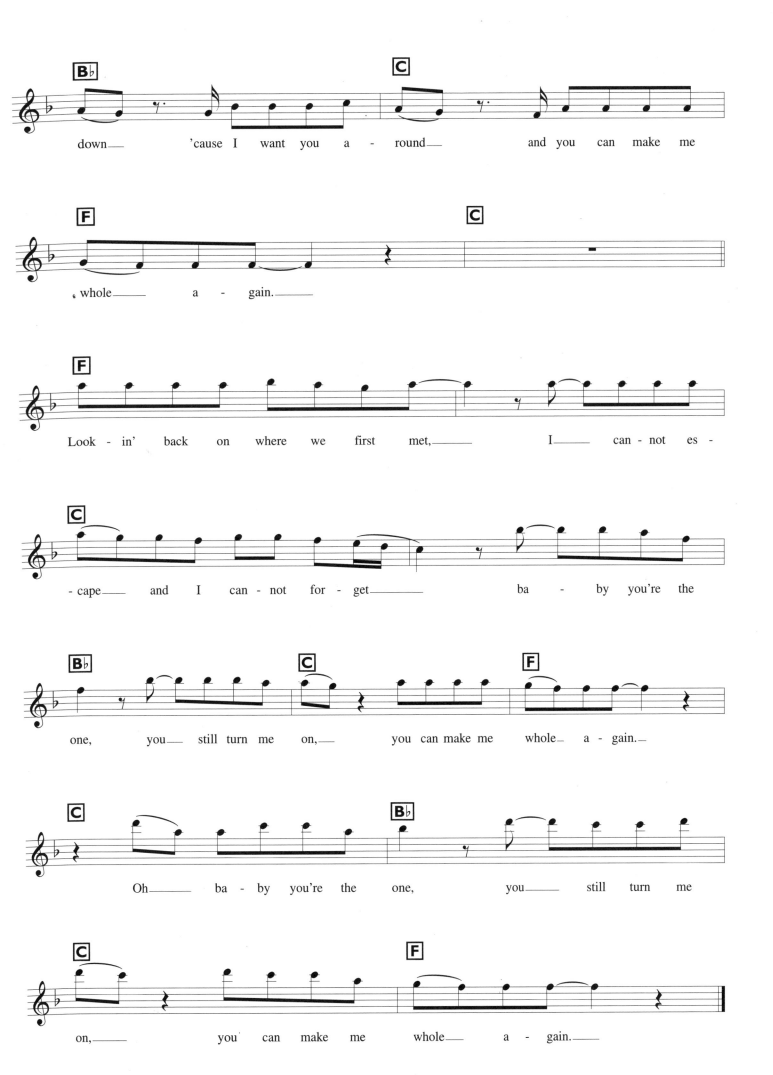

EASIEST KEYBOARD COLLECTION

Easy-to-play melody line arrangements for all keyboards with chord symbols and lyrics. Suggested registration, rhythm and tempo are included for each song together with keyboard diagrams showing left-hand chord voicings used.

 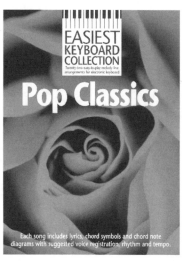 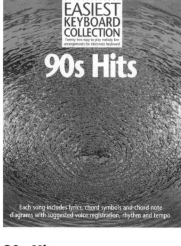 

Showstoppers

Consider Yourself (Oliver!), Do You Hear The People Sing? (Les Misérables), I Know Him So Well (Chess), Maria (West Side Story), Smoke Gets In Your Eyes (Roberta) and 17 more big stage hits.
Order No. AM944218

Pop Classics

A Whiter Shade Of Pale (Procol Harum), Bridge Over Troubled Water (Simon & Garfunkel), Crocodile Rock (Elton John) and 19 more classic hit songs, including Hey Jude (The Beatles), Imagine (John Lennon), and Massachusetts (The Bee Gees).
Order No. AM944196

90s Hits

Over 20 of the greatest hits of the 1990s, including Always (Bon Jovi), Fields Of Gold (Sting), Have I Told You Lately (Rod Stewart), One Sweet Day (Mariah Carey), Say You'll Be There (Spice Girls), and Wonderwall (Oasis).
Order No. AM944229

Abba

A great collection of 22 Abba hit songs. Includes: Dancing Queen, Fernando, I Have A Dream, Mamma Mia, Super Trouper, Take A Chance On Me, Thank You For The Music, The Winner Takes It All, and Waterloo.
Order No. AM959860

Also available...

Ballads, Order No. AM952116   **The Corrs**, Order No. AM959849
The Beatles, Order No. NO90686   **Elton John**, Order No. AM958320
Boyzone, Order No. AM958331   **Film Themes**, Order No. AM952050
Broadway, Order No. AM952127   **Hits of the 90s,** Order No. AM955780
Celine Dion, Order No. AM959850   **Jazz Classics**, Order No. AM952061
Chart Hits, Order No. AM952083   **Love Songs**, Order No. AM950708
Christmas, Order No. AM952105   **Pop Hits**, Order No. AM952072
Classic Blues, Order No. AM950697   **60s Hits**, Order No. AM955768
Classics, Order No. AM952094   **80s Hits**, Order No. AM955779

...plus many more!